Algrove Publishing Limited
36 Mill Street
Almonte, Ontario
Canada K0A 1A0

Telephone: (613) 256-0350
Fax: (613) 256-0360
Email: sales@algrove.com

National Library of Canada Cataloguing in Publication

Jernberg, John
    Forging / John Jernberg.

(Classic reprint series)
Reprint. Originally published: Chicago : American Technical
      Society, 1918.
Includes index.
ISBN 1-894572-93-9

      1. Forging. I. Title. II. Series: Classic reprint series (Almonte, Ont.)

TT215.J47 2004   682'.4   C2003-906504-9

Printed in Canada
#2-03-04

Publisher's Note

Blacksmithing is among the most ancient of crafts. It flourished worldwide until a few hundred years ago when the casting of iron began to supplant the activity in many fields. The problem with casting (until recently) was that the most economical form, iron casting, resulted in a relatively brittle product. Only when steam power developed was it possible to bridge the two metal forming methods with power forging, particularly drop forging, which was an amalgam of the two processes. It could reliably produce high tolerance shapes that could better cope with the stresses dictated by the new equipment designs of the industrial revolution.

John Jernberg neatly ties the art of blacksmithing to the science of forging, its true successor in the metalworking field.

Leonard G. Lee,
Publisher
November 2003
Almonte, Ontario

Warning

This is a reprint of a book published in 1918. It describes what was done and what was recommended to be done in accordance with the knowledge and practices of the day. It should be read in this light.

For example, the suggested use of cyanide of potassium is mentioned in a few places in this book.

Fortunately current laws on the control of poisonous substances make it, and others, difficult to obtain but you should always question similar advice in old books or reprints of old books.

We used to treat lead casually until we found that it accumulated in our systems. Treat all chemicals with respect and always use them only in ways sanctioned by the sellers and the law.

FORGING

MANUAL OF PRACTICAL INSTRUCTION IN HAND FORGING OF
WROUGHT IRON, MACHINE STEEL, AND TOOL STEEL;
DROP FORGING; AND HEAT TREATMENT OF
STEEL, INCLUDING ANNEALING, HARD-
ENING, AND TEMPERING

BY

JOHN JERNBERG

INSTRUCTOR IN FORGE PRACTICE AND HEAT TREATMENT OF STEEL
WORCESTER POLYTECHNIC INSTITUTE
MEMBER, SWEDISH ENGINEERING SOCIETY

ILLUSTRATED

AMERICAN TECHNICAL SOCIETY
CHICAGO
1918

INTRODUCTION

THE art of blacksmithing is an ancient one and for centuries, probably, was the only metal-working profession. With the development of the method of casting iron, the cheapness of this useful process brought about a wider adoption of cast-iron forms than was justified by the fragile nature of the castings used. In later years the fields of usefulness of the two types of metal work have been very definitely fixed by the requirements of construction, the element of tensile strength, and the expansion of the methods of production manufacturing. The development of drop forging had also a marked effect upon the return to forging methods, particularly in the small tool field, the skill in the use of power hammers and the use of gang dies having made forging the very cheapest possible method of manufacture.

¶ In the last few years the adoption of so many new types of steel—particularly of the high-speed and self-hardening variety —has made extensive demands on the machinist's knowledge of heat treatment of these metals. In fact, the importance of heat treatment is often lost sight of in the business of selecting a certain type of steel for a given class of work. The composition of the steel and the processes of forging, annealing, hardening, and tempering the stock are of vital importance in producing a finished article which will endure, and it therefore behooves every metal worker to look carefully to the acquirement of the information necessary to handle this kind of work.

¶ The author of this article has had many years of experience, not only in practical work but also in the field of instruction, and therefore the information which he has given should be doubly valuable. This discussion of the heat treatment of steel is particularly timely and is the result of many experiments with different types of steel. It is the hope of the publishers that the treatise will prove of distinct value, not only to the trained man but to the layman who wishes to keep abreast of the times.

CONTENTS

MECHANICAL DETAILS

	PAGE
Materials and equipment	1
Forging materials	1
Heating apparatus	2
Forges	2
Furnaces	7
Common tools	9
Hammers	9
Sledges	10
Anvils	10
Tongs	12
Swages	13
Machine tools	15
Drop hammers	15
Power hammers	16
Presses	18
Bulldozers	19
Bolt headers	19
Cranes	19
Forging operations	20
Smith welding	20
Welding heat	20
Scale	21
Fluxes	21
Scarfing	22
Lap welding	22
Butt welding	26
Split welding	27
Angle welding	27
T-welding	28
Simple bend forging	29
Forging operations	29
Calculation of stock for bent shapes	33
Bend types	35
Medium forged work	49
Calculation of stock	49
Standard large types	54
Tool-steel work	67
Standard forms	67
Miscellaneous processes	78
Shrinking	78
Brazing	80
Bending cast iron	81

CONTENTS

PAGE

Forging operations (continued)

Miscellaneous processes
Pipe bending.. 81
Duplicate work... 82
Die forging.. 83
Heavy forging.. 85
Drop forging.. 90

HEAT TREATMENT

Heating for forging.. 96
Uniform heating essential....................................... 96
Proper forging heat... 97
Test of heat effect.. 98

Annealing.. 98
General process... 98
High-speed steel.. 99
Copper and brass... 100

Hardening.. 100
Carbonizing.. 105
Cyanide hardening.. 112
Casehardening.. 113
Tool work.. 113
Measuring and testing instruments............................... 116
Pyrometers.. 116
Shore scleroscope.. 121

Tempering.. 123
Essentials of process.. 123
Reduction of brittleness.. 124
Baths for tempering.. 125
Furnaces for tempering.. 127

GAS HEATING FURNACE
Courtesy of American Gas Furnace Company, New York City

FORGING

PART I

MECHANICAL DETAILS

MATERIALS AND EQUIPMENT

Forging Materials. Forging in general treats of the hammering, working, or forming of heated metals. The materials upon which forging or blacksmithing is done, are wrought iron and steel. As explained in "Metallurgy", wrought iron is an iron from which the silicon, phosphorus, and most of the carbon has been removed. Steel usually contains some of the impurities that are characteristic of cast iron with the marked peculiarity of holding a varying percentage of carbon. Mild steels are so called on account of the small amount of carbon which they contain. As the percentage of carbon increases, it becomes more difficult to weld the metal. Greater care must also be used in heating lest the metal be burned and its strength destroyed. Until recently all heavy forgings involving welding were made of wrought iron, but now it is customary to make most forgings of mild steel, particularly large ones, although wrought iron is somewhat more satisfactory where a great amount of welding is required.

Classes. These metals may be roughly divided into three general classes, although the division line may not be sharply drawn between any two classes, as follows: (1) wrought iron; (2) machine steel; and (3) tool steel. The characteristics and method of manufacture of the metals are described in "Metallurgy." A rough distinction such as a blacksmith would use is about as follows: Wrought iron has a fibrous structure with stringy streaks of slag running lengthwise of the bar, giving it a decided fiber similar to wood. Machine steel, more properly described as mild steel, or sometimes called soft steel, has much the same properties as wrought iron excepting that it lacks the fiber and is somewhat stronger. Tool steel differs from the other two materials in the fact that by suddenly cooling from a high heat it may be made very hard, or hardens, to use the technical term. Wrought iron or machine steel are not hardened by the same treatment. Tool steel is practically the same thing as wrought iron or machine steel with a small percentage of carbon added. In fact, either of the two metals may be turned into tool steel by the addition of carbon. This principle is used in casehardening. Norway iron or Swedish iron is a grade of very pure wrought iron containing little slag. It is more expensive than ordinary wrought iron. Refined iron is a grade of wrought iron not as good as Norway iron but better than ordinary iron. Norway iron costs about twice as much as machine steel, which is somewhat cheaper than wrought iron of almost any grade. Machine steel, made by both the open-hearth and Bessemer processes, is used for forging.

Sizes of Stock. Material from which forgings are ordinarily made comes to the forge shop in the shape of bars having uniform sections throughout; generally round, square, or rectangular in section, and varying from $\frac{1}{8}$ inch thick to 18 inches square. Heavier sizes may be had to order. Bars are ordinarily 12 to 20 feet in length. Thin stuff, $\frac{1}{8}$ inch or less in thickness, usually comes in strips of about 40 feet. This may be had from stock up to 6 or 8 inches wide. Tool steel also comes in bars generally about 6 or 8 feet long. The ordinary sizes of tool-steel stock are known as *base sizes* and the price is fixed on these base sizes. Stock of a larger or smaller size than the base sizes is generally charged for at an increase in price. Thus inch-square tool steel, which is a base size, is worth in certain grades about 14 cents a pound. Steel of exactly the same grade and character, $\frac{3}{16}$ of an inch square, costs about 18 cents.

Classification of Equipment. The outfit of a forge shop consists in general of the heating apparatus—the forge, furnaces, etc.; and the handling equipment—the anvil, the various tools, and the machines for shaping and working.

HEATING APPARATUS

Forges. While forges or fires are of many shapes and sizes, the principles of their construction remain the same. An ordinary blacksmith forge is a fireplace in the bottom of which there is a tuyere for admitting a blast of air to blow the fire. Where the air blast is furnished by a hand bellows, the pipe leading therefrom to the tuyere is open throughout. Where a power-driven blower furnishes the blast, there is a valve in the pipe for regulating it.

The usual form of tuyere consists of a single blast pipe, opening into the bottom of the fire pit. This may be a simple nozzle as in Fig. 1, with the blast regulated by a damper in the pipe; or, it may have a regulator at the mouth of the tuyere as shown. Sometimes the tuyere has several openings, and is then in the form of a grate. Whatever its form, it should be possible to clean it from below,

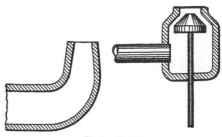

Fig. 1. Tuyere

in order that coal and clinkers falling into it may be removed.

Fig. 2. Modern Forge
Courtesy of Buffalo Forge Company, Buffalo, New York

A modern type of forge is shown in Fig. 2. This is provided with a hood for carrying off the smoke. The pipe connected to the hood extends downward to an underground flue leading to an exhaust fan which draws out the air. The blast pipe is also underground, and a small pipe leads upward to the tuyere, the amount of blast admitted to the fire being regulated by a slide in this pipe. This system of underground piping is known as the down-draft system.

In some shops no provision is made for carrying off the smoke, while in others hoods are placed above the forges and connected to

Fig. 3.   Motor-Driven Exhauster or Blower
Courtesy of Buffalo Forge Company, Buffalo, New York

overhead pipes, which may be either connected to an exhaust fan or led directly to the roof. The down-draft system is the more modern and generally the best.

Blast.   The blast is furnished to the fires of a blacksmith shop by blowers of various kinds. For many years the ordinary bellows was used. This has been superseded by the fan blower which is now almost universally used, even for hand power.

Such a fan blower is shown in Fig. 3. It is formed of a thin cast-iron shell in which there are a set of rapidly revolving blades.

These blades set up a current of air which presses against the side of the shell and escapes through the tangential opening. The pressure of the blast used for an open blacksmith fire varies from about 2 to 7 ounces per square inch. The lower pressure is used for a light fire and light work. The higher pressure is suitable for heavy classes of work.

Fuel. The common fuel for small fires is soft or bituminous coal, coke for large fires and furnaces, and occasionally hard coal in small furnaces. The soft coal used is of a grade known as *smithing coal*. It should be very clean and free from impurities. A lump of good forge coal breaks easily with a crumbly looking fracture and the coal shows clean and bright on all faces. It will not break up into layers as "steaming" coal will, such seamy looking breaks being caused by the more or less earthy impurities. If forge coal splits and shows dull looking streaks or layers, it is poor coal. Good coal has little clinker and breaks easily. When used, the coal is dampened and kept wet before putting on the fire. It should be broken up fine before dampening, and not used in lumps.

Fires. The fire must be carefully watched. It is very important that it should be in first-class condition at all times for the work in hand. A certain depth of fire is always necessary. If the fire be too shallow, the cold blast will penetrate the fire in spots, making it impossible to heat the metal. There should be depth enough to the fire to prevent this. For small work there should be at least three or four inches of fire below the metal that is heating. There should also be thickness enough of fire above the work being heated to prevent the metal from losing heat to the outside air. The fire should be kept as small as possible to heat the work properly. As a general rule the fire will follow the blast. If the fire is wanted larger, it may be made so by loosening the edges of the fire by a bar, allowing the blast to come through around the sides, and causing the fire to spread. When a small fire is wanted the damp coal should be packed down tightly around the sides and the center of the fire loosened up slightly. For light work a small round fire is used. For heavier heating the fire is started by placing a large block on top of the tuyere, on each side of which green coal is packed down hard in the shape of an oblong mound. The block is then removed and the fire started in the hole left. These mounds are left undisturbed and fresh fuel is added to the fire in the shape of coke which has either been previously made by loosely banking a quantity of green coal over the fire and partially burning it to coke, or is bought ready made. With a small fire the fuel is constantly added around the sides where it is turned into coke. This coke is raked into the center of the fire as wanted and more coal added around the sides and patted down to keep the fire in shape.

When too much blast is blown through the fire all the oxygen is not burned out of the air. This attacks the iron, forming a heavy

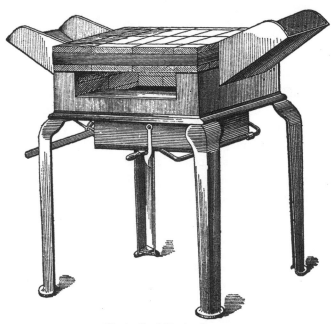

Fig. 4. Small Heating Furnace

coat of oxide or scale (the black scale which falls from heated iron). This sort of fire is known as an *oxidizing fire* and should not be used when it is possible to avoid it. When just enough air is being admitted to keep the fire burning brightly and all of the oxygen is burned, the fire is in good condition for heating. Very little scale is formed and some of the scale already formed may even be turned back to iron. This sort of a fire is known as a *reducing fire*. In other words, when the fire is in condition to give oxygen to anything, it is an oxidizing fire. If in condition to take away oxygen, it is a reducing fire.

Banking. The fire may be kept for some time by placing a block of wood in the center and covering over with fresh coal.

Furnaces. In nearly all manufacturing work and in large work in the jobbing shop, the heating is done in furnaces. The heat is generally supplied by either hard coal, coke, oil, or gas—coke being more commonly employed in jobbing shops. Sometimes ordinary coal is used.

Small Type. A furnace used for heating small work for manufacturing is shown in Fig. 4. This may be used with either ordinary coal or coke. Gas furnaces, a simple type of which for all around work is shown in Fig. 5, are used when an even heat is wanted, particularly for hardening and tempering. For manufacturing work the furnaces are sometimes fixed to do the heating automatically. The pieces to be hardened are carried through the furnace on an endless chain which moves at a speed so timed that the pieces have just time enough to be heated to the right temperature as they pass through the furnace. Such a furnace is shown in Fig. 6.

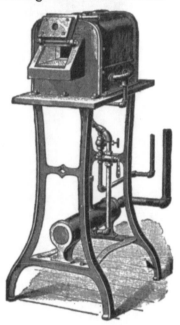

Fig. 5. Simple Gas Furnace
Courtesy of American Gas Furnace Company, New York City

Reverberatory. A reverberatory, or air furnace, is a furnace in which ore, metal, or other material is exposed to the action of flame, but not to the contact of burning fuel. The flame passes over a bridge and then downward upon the material spread upon the hearth. Such furnaces are extensively used in shops where heavy work is being executed. They are also used for melting iron or other metals. For this purpose, however, they are not economical, since they require about twice as much fuel as that used in the cupola for the production of good hot iron. To be effective the flame must be made to reverberate from the low roof of the furnace down upon the hearth and work. The form of the roof and the velocity of the currents determine the hottest part of the furnace.

A common form of reverberatory furnace is shown in Fig. 7. The whole is lined with fire brick from the top of the grates to the

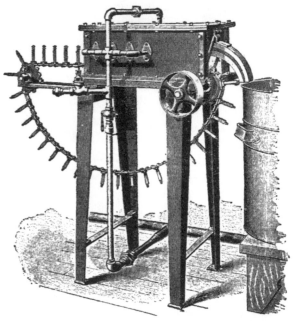

Fig. 6.   Automatic Gas Furnace
Courtesy of American Gas Furnace Company, New York City

top of the stack.   The fuel is burned in a fire box separated from the heating portion of the furnace by a low bridge wall *D*.   Access to

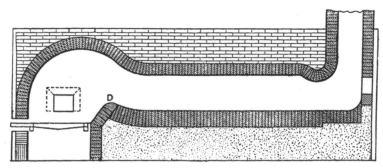

Fig. 7.   Section of Reverberatory Furnace

the grate is obtained by suitable doors both above and below.   When in service, both doors are tightly closed and a strong forced draft is admitted to the ash pit. Beyond the bridge wall is the furnace proper. This usually consists of a low chamber with a level floor. Like the fire box it is completely lined with a thick wall of fire brick. Access is obtained to this chamber through a vertically sliding door. These doors are also lined with fire brick and are usually suspended from chains. These pass over pulleys, and have counterbalancing weights at the other end.

The operation of the furnace is exceedingly simple. After the fuel has been charged upon the grates, the ash-pit and furnace doors are closed; the material to be heated is put upon the floor of the chamber; the doors are closed and the draft admitted to the ash pit. The thick walls which surround the furnace prevent radiation of its heat. The fire brick are, therefore, heated to incandescence and the hot gases sweep through the chamber. The flow of the gases is usually checked by a choke damper on top of the stack.

The outer form of these furnaces is usually rectangular. The brick walls are tied together by stay rods to prevent bulging, and the corners are protected by angle irons.

The selection of the fuel is an important matter in the operation of these furnaces. Experiments have been made with almost every kind of fuel. That now universally used is a soft bituminous coal that will not cake.

Steam or power hammers are always used in connection with these furnaces. The work is too large and heavy for manipulation by hand hammers.

COMMON TOOLS

Hammers. Several kinds of hammers are used in a forge shop. The commonest shape is the ball peen shown at A, Fig. 8. Other kinds are the straight peen and cross peen illustrated at B and C. A square-faced hammer, sometimes called a *blacksmith's hammer*, shown at D, is occasionally used on tool work. Commonly a ball peen hammer of about $1\frac{1}{2}$ pounds weight is used.

In the fitting of the handle to the head great care should be taken. Hammer handles are made elliptical in cross-section. The major axis of this ellipse should exactly coincide with that of the eye of the head. The reason is that the hand naturally grasps the handle so that its major axis lies in the direction of the line of motion.

Hence, unless the handle is properly fitted in this particular, there will be constant danger of striking a glancing blow. The handle should also stand at right angles to a center line drawn from the ball of the peen to the face. The eye in the head is usually so set that the weight on the face side is greater than that on the peen. The effect

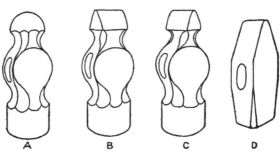
Fig. 8. Common Types of Hammers

of this is to so balance the tool that heavier and more accurate blows can be struck than if the weight were evenly balanced on each side of the eye.

Sledges. Sledges are heavier hammers used by the blacksmith's helper and vary in weight from 5 to 20 pounds. The three common shapes are shown in Fig. 9; *A*, *B*, and *C*, being cross-peen, straight-peen, and double-faced sledges, respectively. A sledge for common

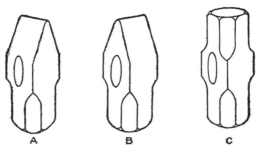
Fig. 9. Common Types of Sledges

work ordinarily weighs about 12 pounds. Sledge handles are generally about 30 to 36 inches long, depending on the nature of the work to be done.

Anvils. Next to the hammer in importance is the anvil. This may be any block of metal upon which the piece to be shaped is laid.

The anvil must be of such a weight that it can absorb the blows that are struck upon it without experiencing any perceptible motion in itself.

The ordinary anvil, Fig. 10, has remained unchanged in form for many hundreds of years. Anvils are sometimes made of special shapes, but the one here shown is the common one. An anvil of this form serves for the execution of any work that may be desired. As now made, the body a is of wrought iron to which a face of hardened steel is welded. From one end there projects the horn b, and the overhang of the body at the other end c is called the tail. At the bottom there are four projections d, called the feet, which serve to increase the base upon which the anvil rests as well as to afford the means for clamping it down into position. In the tail there is

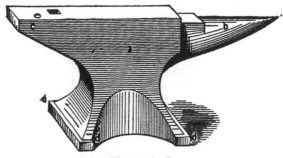

Fig. 10. Anvil

a square hole and a circular hole. The former is called the *hardie hole*, the latter the *spud hole*.

Anvils are also made of cast iron with the working faces chilled, thus giving a sort of casehardening effect.

The anvil should be placed upon the end of a heavy block of wood sunk into the ground to a depth of at least 2 feet, so that it may rest upon a firm but elastic foundation. As the anvil is subjected to constant vibrations, by the nature of the work, it is necessary that it should be firmly fastened to the block.

Weight Classification. Anvils are classed and sold by weight. The weight is generally stamped on the side of the anvil. Three numbers are used. The first to the left shows the weight in English hundredweight of 112 pounds each. The middle number shows the additional quarters of hundredweight and the right-hand figure the number of odd pounds. For instance, an anvil marked 2-3-4 would weigh $2\times112+\frac{3}{4}$ of $112+4$ pounds $=312$ pounds and would be known as about a 300-pound anvil.

Tongs. Next to the hammer and anvil in importance and usage are the tongs. They vary in size from those suitable for hold-

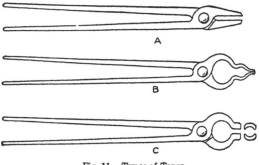

ing the smallest wires to those capable of handling ingots and bars of many tons in weight. The jaws are also adapted to fit over the piece to be handled and are of a great variety of shapes. As the requirements of each piece of work

Fig. 11.　Types of Tongs

vary so much from those which precede and follow it, it is custom-ary for the blacksmith to dress his own tongs and adapt them, from time to time, to the work he has in hand. Comparatively few, therefore, of the various shapes of tongs found in shops are manufactured and for sale. A few of the general types and forms in common use are here given.

A, Fig. 11, shows a pair of flat-jawed tongs, the commonest shape used. *B* is a pair of pick-up tongs used for holding work while tem-

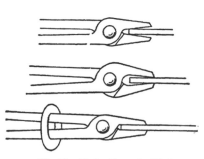

pering, and picking up pieces of hot metal. *C* is a common shape used for holding both square and round iron, the jaws being bent to fit the stock in each case. A modification of this shape is also used for heavy steam-hammer work. Tongs frequently have the jaws made in some special shape for a particular piece of work, the object always being to

Fig. 12.　Fitting Tongs for Work

have the jaws grip the work as firmly as possible.

Fitting Tongs to Work. Tongs must be always carefully fitted to the work. Tongs which take hold of the work as shown at *A* and *B*, Fig. 12, should not be used. The first pair shown have the jaws too

close together, the second, too far apart. When properly fitted the
jaws should touch the work throughout the entire length as shown in
the lower sketch C. To fit tongs the jaws are heated red hot, the piece
to be held placed between them, and the jaws hammered down until
touching their entire length. Tongs which do not fit the work perfectly should never, under any circumstances, be used. When in use
on all but the smallest work, a link is driven over the handles to grip
the tongs in position, as shown.

Set Hammers and Flatters. These tools are used for smoothing
off flat work when finishing. The set hammer, Fig. 13, is used for work-

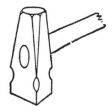

Fig. 13. Set Hammer

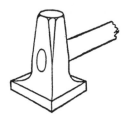

Fig. 14. Flatter

ing up into corners and narrow places. The flatter, Fig. 14, is used on
wide flat surfaces. The face of the set hammer used on light work is
generally about $1\frac{1}{4}$ inches square. That of the flatter about $2\frac{1}{2}$ inches
square, although the sizes vary, depending upon the kind of work.

Swages. Swages, shown in Fig. 15, are used for finishing round
and convex surfaces. The upper
tool is known as the top swage and
is provided with a handle. The
lower one is the bottom swage
and is held in place by a square
stem or shank which extends
downward and fits into the hardie
hole of the anvil. Tools of this
character should never be used
on an anvil where they fit so
tight that it is necessary to drive
them into place. The swages

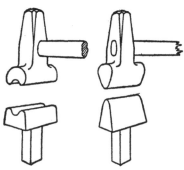

Fig. 15. Swages for Round Work   Fig. 16. Fullers

shown here are used for round work. Swages are also made for
octagonal, hexagonal, and other shapes.

Fullers. Fullers, which are used for working grooves or hollows into shape, are also made top and bottom as shown in Fig. 16.

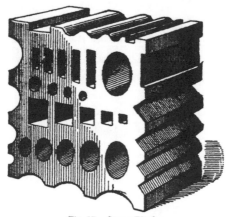

The top fuller is for finishing into round corners, around bosses, and on the inside of angles as illustrated later on. The fuller is also used to spread metal when it is wished to work the metal only in one direction. The metal spreads at right angles to the working edge of the fuller.

Fig. 17.   Swage Block

Swage Blocks. Swage blocks, a common sort of which is shown in Fig. 17, are used for a variety of purposes, mostly for taking the place of bottom swages. These blocks are commonly made from cast iron and weigh about 150 pounds.

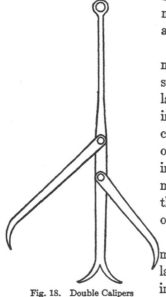

Other Tools. The tools used commonly are calipers, a carpenter's 2-foot steel square, dividers, rule, shovel, tongs, ladle, poker, and a straight bar for loosening the fire. In addition to the ordinary calipers, a blacksmith usually has a pair of double calipers similar to those shown in Fig. 18. With these, two dimensions may be used, one side being set for the thickness, and the other for the width, of the material.

Measuring. When several measurements are to be made particularly on large work, a strip of light stock about $\frac{1}{8}$ inch by 1 inch wide is used. The different dimensions are laid off on this with

Fig. 18.   Double Calipers

chalk or soapstone. In use the strip is held against the work and used in the same manner as a rule. A light rod having a small bent end, made by bending over about $\frac{1}{2}$ inch of stock at right angles, is also sometimes used, particularly when working under the steam hammer. The dimensions may be laid off from the inside of the hooked end. When in use the hooked end is pulled against the end of the material. Soapstone crayon is ordinarily used for marking on iron. The marks do not burn off, but will not show at a red heat. Marks to show at a high heat must be made by nicking the corner of the bar with a chisel or by marking with the center punch. Another common way of making measurements on hot material is to lay off the different distances on the side of the anvil with chalk, the dimensions being laid off from one corner or end.

MACHINE TOOLS

Manufacturing Requirement. The manufacturing shop differs very essentially from the jobbing shop. In the latter shop very few forgings are made at the same time exactly alike, while in manufacturing, each

Fig. 19. Board Drop Hammer
Courtesy of E. W. Bliss Company, Brooklyn, New York

forging is generally duplicated a large number of times and special machines are used for doing the work.

Drop Hammers. Drop hammers are used for quickly forming complicated shapes out of wrought iron or steel. They consist, as the name indicates, of a head that may be "dropped" from any desired height upon the piece to be shaped. The head of the drop and the anvil are in the form of dies into which the metal is forced to flow, and thus take on the form desired. In drop-forging, the metal must be heated to a high temperature so as to be soft and plastic.

A common type of drop hammer used for this kind of work is shown in Fig. 19. The hammer in this case is fastened to a board

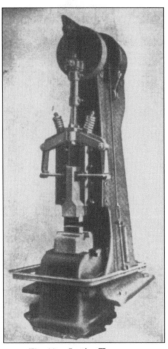

Fig. 20.   Justice Hammer

and is raised by the friction rollers at the top of the frame being pressed against the board. When the hammer reaches the top of the frame it is dropped by releasing the rollers from the board. This may be done automatically or by a foot treadle. Drop hammers are also built in the same general way as steam hammers, as referred to in the sections on Heavy Forging and Drop Forging. Dies for drop forging generally consist of a roughing or breaking-down die where the rough stock is first given approximately the desired shape and a smoothing die when the finishing is done. These dies have in their faces holes of the same shape as the required forging.

Power Hammers. Another tool which is used to quite a large extent in manufacturing, as well as in the jobbing shop, is the power hammer. These are run by belts and are used where a quick rapid blow is wanted. The type shown in Fig. 20 is known as a Justice hammer; that shown in Fig. 21 is a Bradley. Shaped dies are frequently used on these hammers.

Spring-Ram Type. Fig. 22 shows the Beaudry power hammer. This hammer has many claims in its favor—superior elasticity; perfect control of blow struck. These are obtained by a device which is simple and effective, allowing the ram the greatest freedom of throw and causing it to rebound the instant the blow is struck.

This hammer has no beam, saddle, rubber cushions, leather straps, nor coiled springs. Its ram or head is of steel and has an internal curve or track of () shape, as shown by the sectional cut, Fig. 23. Two steel spring arms with hardened tool-steel rollers at their lower extremities operate within the ram which, with increased speed of hammer, acquires increased travel and force of blow.

This simple and positive action of the spring arms perfectly controls the ram and causes it to rebound the instant the blow is

Fig. 21. Bradley Power Hammer

struck, without reaction or jump or sudden undue strains on any of the hammer parts. The elasticity and force of the blow is obtained thus, and by it the full stroke can be had as readily on a piece 4 inches square as on a piece $\frac{1}{8}$ inch in thickness, and no change of adjustment is necessary excepting for unusually heavy work.

The hammer is started, stopped, and regulated by a foot treadle which extends around the base of the machine and through a varying pressure on which there is obtained instantly any desired speed or force of blow of from 1 pound up to its full capacity, which latter is an estimated maximum blow of six times the weight of the ram.

The anvil clears the main frame casting as shown in Fig. 24, allowing any length bars to be worked either way of dies. It is an inde-

Fig. 22.   Beaudry Spring-Ram Power Hammer
Courtesy of Beaudry & Company, Boston,
Massachusetts

pendent casting having no connection with the frame, and thus preventing crystallization of the hammer parts; it is held in place by its own foundation bolts and stands in the center of the hammer foundation. To it is keyed an independent show die and to that in turn is keyed the bottom die.

Presses. Presses may be of either the gear-driven or the hydraulically operated type. They serve the same purpose as drop hammers. They do the work more slowly, however. The class of work is, in some respects, the same, the principal difference lying in peculiarities of shape that require different time intervals for the flow of the metal. Where the shape is such that the

Fig. 23.   Close View of Beaudry
Ram

Fig. 24.   Close View of Beaudry Anvil

metal must move slowly in order to acquire its new shape or fill the die, the press should be used.

Flanging Type. A particular type of forging press is the flanging press. This is used more particularly in boiler work and is generally a heavy hydraulic press. The flanging is done by placing the heated metal on the bed of the press and closing the dies together by hydraulic pressure.

Bulldozer. This is a tool used for bending and consists of a heavy cast-iron bed with a block or bolster at one end, and a moving head which slides back and forth on the bed. A common type is shown in Fig. 25. Heavy dies are clamped against the bolster and

Fig. 25. Bulldozer—Used for Bending Stock
Courtesy of Williams, White & Company, Moline, Illinois

on the moving head, of such a shape and in such a way that when the moving head is nearest the bolster, the shape left between the two dies is exactly the shape to which it is desired to bend the stock. In operation, the moving head slides back and forth on the bed. The bar to be bent is heated and placed between the dies when the head is farthest from the bolster. A clutch is then thrown in and the head moves forward to the bolster, bending the iron as it goes.

Bolt Headers. These are really upsetting machines that form the heads of bolts upon straight rods. Owing to the rapidity with which they do their work, they are invariably used for manufacturing bolts in quantities.

Cranes. Where heavy work is to be handled, it is necessary to have some means of conveying the work from one part of the shop to another. This is done by means of cranes of two general types: (1) the traveling crane; and (2) the jib crane. The former type runs on an overhead track from one end of the shop to the other, generally.

Jib Type. The jib crane type is used more commonly for handling work under the hammers, and is merely an arm or boom swinging around a post and having a suitable arrangement for raising and lowering the work. When handling heavy work, whenever possible, it is suspended from the crane by its center, in such a way that it nearly balances. The suspending is generally done by means of an endless chain such as illustrated in Fig. 26, and in this way it may be easily rolled and swung from side to side. For ease in handling large forgings, a bar or handle known as a *porter bar* is sometimes welded on.

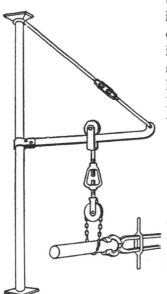

Fig. 26.   Work Supported by Jib Crane

FORGING OPERATIONS

SMITH WELDING

Nature of Process. If a piece of steel or iron is heated, the metal becomes softer as the temperature is raised. Finally a heat is reached, called the welding heat, at which the metal is so soft that, if two pieces similarly heated are placed in contact, they will stick. If the pieces so heated are placed together and hammered, they may be joined in one piece. This process is known as *welding*.

Welding Heat. The greatest difficulty in welding is to heat properly, which must be done evenly and cleanly. If the temperature is raised too high, the iron will burn, throwing off bright star-like sparks. If the temperature is too low, the pieces will not stick to each other. The proper heat can only be determined by experimenting, which may be easily done by doubling over a piece of scrap iron for 2 or 3 inches and welding into a solid piece.

As the welding heat is reached, in heating wrought iron and mild steel, small particles of the metal are melted and blown upward from the fire by the blast, and as these small particles come in contact with the air, they burn and form small explosive sparks like little white stars. Whenever these sparks are seen coming from the fire, it is a sure indication that the iron is burning. They are sometimes used as a sort of an indication of the welding heat, but the only sure way of determining the heat is by the appearance of the heated iron, which might be described as sort of creamy white. The welding heat is sometimes described as a white heat. This is not correct, because iron or steel is never raised to a white heat even when melted, as may be easily proved by comparing a piece of wrought iron at welding heat, with an ordinary arc lamp.

Scale. When two pieces of metal are welded together there must be nothing between them. Heated iron or steel is always covered with scale (iron oxide). This scale, if allowed to stay on the surfaces to be joined, will prevent a good weld. It is necessary when welding, to heat the iron or steel to a high enough temperature to melt this scale and when the two pieces are put together, if the joint or scarf is properly made, most of this melted scale is easily forced from between the two pieces, leaving the clean surfaces of the metal in contact. This scale only melts at a very high heat, much higher than the heat at which it would be possible to weld the iron if it could be kept free from scale.

Fluxes. Fluxes are used to lower the melting point of the scale. The flux is sprinkled on the surfaces to be joined just before the metal reaches the welding heat. The metal is then put back into the fire, raised to the welding heat and the weld made as usual. The scale is acted upon by the flux and melts at a lower heat than when no flux is used. As the flux melts it spreads or runs over the hot metal and forms a sort of protective covering, which, by keeping out the air, prevents to a large extent the formation of more scale. The flux in no way acts as a cement or glue to stick the pieces together, but merely helps to melt off the scale already formed, and prevents the formation of more.

Sand and Borax. These substances are common fluxes. Sand may be used when welding wrought iron and machine steel; borax is substituted for sand for fine work and when welding tool steel.

Borax is a better flux, as it melts at a lower temperature than sand, and thus makes welding possible at a lower heat. Borax and sal ammoniac (ammonium-chloride) are sometimes mixed and used as a welding compound or flux, the proportion being about 4 parts borax to 1 part sal ammoniac. This mixture is also a good flux for brazing. Borax contains a large amount of water which makes it boil and foam when melting and in this condition is very liable to drop away from the heating metal. If borax is heated red hot and allowed to cool, the water is driven off and the borax is left in a glass-like condition. Borax treated this way and then powdered is the best for welding, as it melts and sticks to the metal without any boiling.

Welding Compounds. These are fluxes serving the same purpose as sand or borax. Some of the better ones use borax as a basis. Some of these compounds are first class for their purpose and others are not so good, being simply intended as cheap substitutes for borax.

Processes

Scarfing. For most welding the ends of the pieces to be joined must be so shaped that when welded they make a smooth joint.

Fig. 27. Work Scarfed for Lap Weld

This shaping of the ends is known as scarfing, and the shaped end is called a scarf. The scarfed ends should not fit tightly before welding but should be so shaped that they touch in the center of the joint, leaving the sides somewhat open. In this way, when the weld is made, the melted scale is forced from between the pieces. If the scarfs were made to touch on the edge of the joint, leaving the center hollow, the scale not having a chance to escape would be held in the center of the joint, leaving a weak place, and making a bad weld.

Lap Welding. This is the common weld used for joining flat bars together. The ends to be welded are scarfed or shaped as

shown in Fig. 27.   In preparing, the ends of the pieces to be welded
should be first upset until they are considerably thicker than the
rest of the bar.   This is done to allow for the iron that burns off or is
lost by scaling, and also to allow for the hammering when welding
the pieces together.   To make a proper weld the joint should be well
hammered, and as this reduces the size of the iron at that point, the
pieces must be upset to allow for this reduction in size.   For light

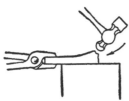

Fig. 28.   Shaping Scarf

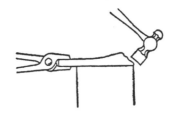

Fig. 29.   Finishing Scarf

work the scarfing may be done with a hand hammer.   For heavy
work a fuller and sledge should be used.   After upsetting on light
work, the end to be scarfed is roughly shaped with the peen end
of the hammer as illustrated in Fig. 28, the final finishing being done
with the flat face of the hammer.

For this work (finishing the edge of the scarf) as well as for all
pointed work, the end of the bar should be brought to the extreme
edge of the anvil in the manner indicated in Fig. 29.   In this way a
hard blow may be struck with the
center of the face of the hammer
without danger of striking the hammer
on the anvil.   For all ordinary lap
welding the length of the scarf may
be about $1\frac{1}{2}$ times the thickness of the
bar.   Thus, on a bar $\frac{1}{2}$ inch thick, the

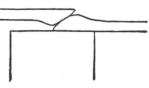

Fig. 30.   Overlapping for Weld

scarf will be about $\frac{3}{4}$ of an inch long.   The width of the end, Fig. 27,
should be slightly less than the width of the bar.   In welding the
pieces together the first piece held by the helper should be placed
scarf side up on the anvil and the second piece laid on top, scarf
side down, overlapping them to about the amount shown in Fig. 30.
As it is generally somewhat difficult to lay the top piece directly in

place, it should be steadied by resting lightly against the corner of the anvil and thus guided into place.

Round Lap Weld. This is the weld used to join round bars end to end to form a continuous bar. All the precautions regarding the scarf, etc., used for making the lap weld should be taken with this as well. The general shape of the scarf is shown in Fig. 27. It will be noticed that the end is hammered to a sharp point. If the scarf be made with a flat or chisel-shaped end similar to the flat lap weld, the corners will project beyond the sides of the bar in welding and cause considerable trouble, as it will then be necessary to work entirely around the bar before the joint is closed down. With

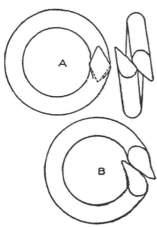

Fig. 31.   Lapping Ring Ends

a pointed scarf the weld may be frequently made by hammering on two sides only. This is not so important when welding between swages.

Ring Round Stock. When a ring is made, the exact amount of stock may be cut, the ends upset and scarfed as though making a round lap weld, the stock bent into shape, as shown in Fig. 31, and welded. The ends should be lapped sideways as shown at *A*. In this position a ring may be welded by simply laying it flat on the anvil, while if lapped the other way, *B*, one end in, the other out, it would be necessary to do the welding over the horn of the anvil. In all welding the piece should be so lapped that the hammering may be done in the quickest and easiest manner.

Allowance for Welding. In work of this character, when the stock is cut to a certain length, allowance is sometimes made for loss due to welding. The exact amount is hard to determine, depending on how carefully the iron is heated and the number of heats required to make the weld. The only real loss which occurs in welding is the amount which is burned off and lost in scale. Of course, when preparing for the weld, the ends of the pieces are upset and the stock consequently shortened. The piece is still further shortened by overlapping the ends when making the weld, but as all of this material is afterward hammered back into shape, no loss occurs. No rules can be given for the loss in welding, but as a rough guide on small work, a length of stock equal to from $\frac{1}{4}$ to $\frac{3}{4}$ of the thickness of the

bar will probably be about right for waste. Work of this kind should be watched very closely and the stock measured before and after welding in order to determine exactly how much stock is lost.

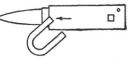

Fig. 32. Scarfing Chain Link

Chain Links. The first step in making a chain link is to bend the stock into a U-shape, care being taken to have the legs of the U exactly even in length. The scarf used is approximately the pointed shape used for a round lap-weld scarf. An easy method is as fol-

lows: One end of the U-shaped piece is laid on the anvil as indicated in Fig. 32. This is flattened by striking directly down with the flat face of the hammer, the piece being moved slightly to the left, as shown by the arrow, after each blow, until the end is reached.

This operation leaves a series of lit-tle steps at the end of the piece and works it out in a more or less pointed

Fig. 33. Shaping and Finishing Scarf

shape, as shown in Fig. 33 at *A*. The point should be finished by placing it over the horn of the anvil and touching up with a few light blows. After scarfing the other end of the U in the same

manner the, ends are overlapped as indicated at *B* and welded together. The second link is scarfed, spread open, and the first link inserted. It is then closed up again and welded. The third is joined on this, etc. When made on a commercial scale, light links are not always scarfed

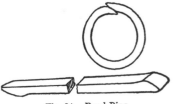

Fig. 34. Band Ring

but sometimes simply hammered together and welded in one heat. This is not possible in ordinary work.

Band Ring. A method of making a band ring from iron bent flatways is illustrated in Fig. 34. Stock is cut to length, the ends upset and scarfed, using a regular flat-weld scarf, and the ring bent into shape and welded; the welding being done over the horn of the anvil. The heating must be carefully done or the outside lap will

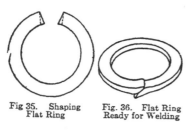

be burned before the inside is nearly hot enough to weld.

Flat or Washer Ring. This is a ring made by bending flat iron edgeways. The ends of the stock are first upset but not scarfed, except for careful work, the ring bent into shape, and the corners

Fig 35.   Shaping
Flat Ring

Fig. 36.   Flat Ring
Ready for Welding

trimmed off on radial lines as shown in Fig. 35.   The ends are then scarfed with a fuller or peen of a hammer and lapped over ready for

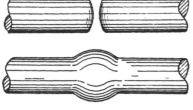

welding as shown in Fig. 36.

Butt Welding. When pieces are simply welded together end to end, making a square joint through the weld, it is known as a butt weld. It is best when making a weld of this kind to round the ends slightly, as illustrated in Fig. 37.   The ends are

Fig. 37.   Typical Butt Weld Before and After
Welding

heated and driven together and this round shape forces out the scale and leaves a clean joint.   As the pieces are driven together they are

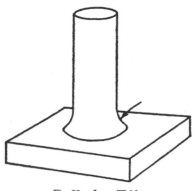

more or less upset at the joint, making a sort of a burr.   This upset part should be worked down at a welding heat between swages.   A butt weld is not as safe or as strong as a lap weld. Long pieces may be butt-welded by placing one piece in the fire from each side.   When the welding heat is reached the pieces are placed end to end, one piece "backed up" with a heavy

Fig. 38.   Jump Weld

weight, and the weld made by striking with a sledge hammer.

Jump Weld. Another form of butt weld shown in Fig. 38 is a jump weld which, however, is a form that should be avoided as much as possible, as it is very liable to be weak. In making a weld of this kind, the piece to be butted on the other should have its end upset in such a manner as to flare out and form sort of a flange, the wider the better. When the weld is made, this flange may be worked down with a fuller or set hammer, thus making a fairly strong weld.

Split Welding Heavy Stock. Heavy stock is sometimes welded by using a scarf of the shape shown in Fig. 39. One piece is split and shaped into a **Y** while the other has its end brought to a blunt point. When properly shaped, the pieces are heated to the welding heat and driven together. The ends of the **Y** are then closed down over the other piece and the weld completed. A second heat is sometimes taken to do this. This weld is often used when joining tool steel to iron or to machine steel. Sometimes the pieces are placed together before taking the welding heat.

Fig. 39. Cleft or Split Weld

Angle Welding. In all welding it should be remembered that the object of the scarfing is to so shape the pieces to be welded that they will form a joint easy to weld and give the proper size for the work. Frequently there are several equally good methods of scarfing for the same sort of a weld, and it should be remembered that the method given here is not necessarily the only way in which that particular weld may be made. Fig. 40 shows one way of scarfing for a right-angled weld made of

Fig. 40. Right-Angled Weld

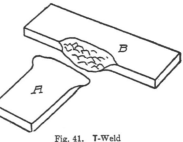

Fig. 41. T-Weld

flat iron. Both pieces are scarfed exactly alike, the scarfing being done by the peen end of the hammer. If necessary, the ends of the pieces may be upset before scarfing. Care should be used to see that the pieces touch first in the center of the scarf, otherwise a pocket will be formed which will retain the scale and spoil the weld.

T=Welding. A method of scarfing for a T-weld is illustrated in Fig. 41. The scarf is formed mostly with the peen end of the hammer; the points are short for easy welding. The stem *A* should be placed on the bar *B*, when welding, so that there is a little lap-over.

Round-Stock T-Weld. Two methods of scarfing for a T-weld made from round stock are shown in Fig. 42. The scarfs are formed mostly with the peen end of the hammer. The illustration will explain itself. The stock should be well upset in either method.

Welding Tool Steel. The general method of scarfing is the same in all welding but greater care must be used in heating when

Fig. 42.   Method of Making T-Weld for Round Stock

welding tool steel. The flux used for welding tool steel should be the sal ammoniac and borax mixture mentioned before. Spring steel or low-carbon steel may be satisfactorily welded if care is used. To weld steel successfully the following precautions should be observed. Clean the fire of all cinders and ashes.

Put sufficient coal upon the fire so that it will be unnecessary to add more coal while taking the welding heat. Upset both pieces near the end and scarf carefully. When possible, punch a hole and rivet the two pieces together. Heat the steel to a full red heat and sprinkle with borax. Replace in the fire and raise to the welding heat. Clean the scarfed surface and strike lightly at first, following with heavier blows. The appearance of steel when at a welding heat is a pale straw color. Always avoid a weld of high-carbon steel alone, when possible.

Welding Steel and Wrought Iron. Steel may also be welded to wrought iron. This is done in the manufacturing of edged tools. The body of the tool is of iron, to which a piece of steel is welded to form the cutting edge. This class of work is best done with a fire of anthracite coal, though coke or charcoal may be used. The fire should be burning brightly when the heating is done. Lay the iron and steel on the coal until they are red hot. Then sprinkle the surfaces of both with the flux and let it vitrify. A convenient method of doing this is to have the powdered flux (borax preferred) in a pepper pot. As soon as the heat has changed the metals to a straw color lay them together and strike. A single blow of a drop hammer, or four or five with a light sledge will do the work. Be sure that these pieces are well covered with a flux before attempting to weld.

SIMPLE BEND FORGING
Fundamental Forging Operations

Shaping. After the metal has been heated it is shaped with the hammer. This shaping may consist of drawing, upsetting, or bending. In drawing a bar of iron it is made longer and of smaller diameter. Upsetting consists of shortening the bar with a corresponding increase of diameter. This work is usually done with the assistance of a helper using a sledge hammer; the smith using a light hand hammer. They strike alternate blows. The helper must watch the point upon which the smith strikes and strike in the same place. Where two helpers are employed the smith strikes after each man. A blow on the anvil by the smith is a signal to stop striking.

Finishing. As the hammer usually marks the metal, it is customary to leave the metal a little full and to finish by the use of flatters and swages. This applies to work that has been shaped under the sledge. Light work can be dressed smoothly, and the hammer can be made to obliterate its own marks.

Drawing Out. In drawing out, as well as in all other forging operations where heavy work is to be done, it is always best to heat the work to as high a temperature as the metal will stand
without injury. Work can
sometimes be drawn out much
faster by working over the horn
of the anvil than on the face,
the reason being this: When a
piece of work is hammered on

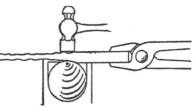

Fig. 43.   Method of Drawing Out Work

the anvil face it flattens out and spreads nearly as much in width as it does in length, working it out longer and wider. As the piece is not wanted wider but merely longer, all the work spent in increasing the width of the stock is wasted. If the hammering is done over the horn of the anvil as illustrated in Fig. 43, the rounded horn acts as a blunt wedge, forcing the metal lengthwise and thus utilizes almost the entire energy of a blow in stretching the metal in the desired direction. Fullers are also used to serve the same purpose and when working under the steam hammer a round bar

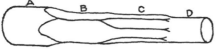

Fig. 44. Drawing Down Round Bar

sometimes takes the place of the fuller or horn of the anvil.

Round Stock. When drawing out or pointing round stock, it should always first be forged down square to the required size and then rounded up in as few blows as possible. Fig. 44 illustrates, in a general way, the different steps in drawing down a round bar from a large to a smaller size, the first step being to hammer it down square as at *B*. This square shape is then made octagonal as at *C* and the octagon is

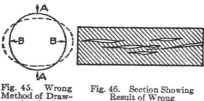

Fig. 45. Wrong Method of Drawing Out

Fig. 46. Section Showing Result of Wrong Drawing

finally rounded up as at *D*. If an attempt be made to hammer the bar by pounding it round and round without the preliminary squaring, the bar is very liable to split through the center, the action being a

good deal as illustrated in Fig. 45, the effect of the blow coming as shown by the arrows *A*. The metal is squeezed together in this direction and forced apart in the direction at right angles as indicated by the arrows *B*. Then, if the piece be slightly rolled for another blow, the sides will roll by each other, and cracks and splits will sooner

Fig. 47. Irregular Shapes

Fig. 48. Method of Squaring Up Bad Corners

or later develop, leaving the bar, if it should be sawed through the center, in a good deal the shape shown in Fig. 46. Particular care should be taken in making conical points as it is almost impossible to work stock to a round point unless the point be first forged down to a square or pyramidal shape.

Truing Up Work. In drawing out it often happens that the bar becomes worked into an irregular or diamond shape, similar to the section shown in Fig. 47. To remedy this, and square up the bad corners, the bar should be laid across the anvil and worked much as shown in Fig. 48, the blows coming in the direction indicated by the arrow. Just as the hammer strikes the work it should be given a sort of sliding motion. No attempt should be made to square up a corner by striking squarely down upon the work. The hammering should all be done in such a way as to force the metal back into the bar and away from the high corner.

Upsetting. When a piece is worked in such a way that its length is shortened and either or both its thickness and width increased, the piece is said to be upset and the operation is known as *upsetting*. There are several methods of upsetting, the one used depending largely upon the shape of the work. In short pieces the work is generally stood on end on the anvil, the hammering being done directly down upon the upper end. The work should always be kept straight, and as soon as a

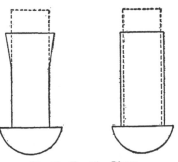

Fig. 49.   Upsetting Rivets

bend or kink is started, it should be straightened out. When a long piece is to be upset it is generally swung back and forth horizontally and the upsetting done by ramming the end against the anvil. The effect of the blow has a decided influence upon the shape of the upset piece, as shown in Fig. 49. Light blows affect the metal for a short distance only, as shown by the swelled out end; the heavier blows are felt more uniformly throughout the entire length.

When rivets are to be driven to fill holes tightly, the blows should be heavy, thus upsetting the rivet tightly into the holes. If a rivet is wanted to hold two pieces together in such a way that they may move, as for instance the rivet in a pair of tongs, the head should be formed with light blows, thus working only the end of the rivet. The part of the work which is heated to the highest temperature is the part which will be most upset, and when upsetting is wished at one point only, that point should be heated to the highest temperature, leaving the other parts of the bar as cold as possible. Upsetting long pieces is sometimes done by raising the piece and allowing it to drop on a heavy cast-iron plate set in the floor. These plates are known as upsetting plates.

Fig. 50.   Punch for Round Holes

Punching. Two kinds of punches are commonly used for making holes in hot metal; the straight hand punch used with a hand hammer, and the one used for heavier stock, provided with a handle and used with a sledge hammer. Punches should of course be made of tool steel. For punching small holes in thin iron a hand punch is ordinarily used. This is a bar of round or octagonal

Fig. 51.   Punch for Heavy and Fast Work

steel, 8 or 10 inches in length, with the end forged down tapering to the same shape, but slightly smaller than the hole to be punched. Such a punch for round holes is shown in Fig. 50. The end of the punch should be perfectly square across, not at all rounding. For heavier and faster work with a helper, a punch similar to Fig. 51 is used, the striking being done with a sledge hammer.

Correct Hand Method. Fig. 52 illustrates the successive steps in punching a clean hole through a piece of hot iron. The work

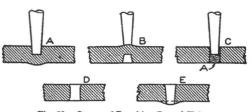

Fig. 52.   Stages of Punching Round Hole

is first laid flat on the anvil and the punch driven about half way through as shown at *A*. This compresses the metal directly underneath the end of the punch and raises a slight bulge on the opposite side of the bar. The piece is then turned over and the punch driven into the bar from this side (the hole being located by the bulge) while the bar is lying flat on the anvil. The punch should be driven about half way through, leaving the work as at *C*. The bar is then moved over the small round hole in the end of the anvil, or is placed on some object having a hole slightly larger than the hole to be punched, and the punch is driven clear through, forcing out the small piece A and leaving the hole as shown at D. It would seem easier to drive the punch completely through the work from one side. If this were done, however, the hole would be left as shown at E; one side would be rounded in, and the other side would be bulged out, while the hole would have a decided taper, being larger at the end from which the punching was done. If the piece is thick, a little powdered coal is put in the hole after it is started, to prevent the punch from sticking to some extent.

Calculation of Stock for Bent Shapes

Mathematical Calculation. *Angles.* It is always convenient and frequently necessary to know the exact amount of stock required to make a given piece of work. There are four general methods

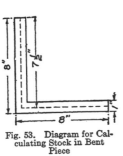
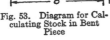

Fig. 53. Diagram for Calculating Stock in Bent Piece

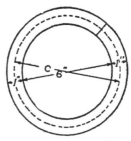

Fig. 54. Diagram for Calculating Stock in Ring

used for determining this. The first and most accurate method, if it can be used conveniently, is mathematical calculation. Taking as an example the bent piece illustrated in Fig. 53. If the outside of this is measured, it would seem as though 16 inches of stock were required. If the inside is measured, 14 inches would seem the proper amount. It has been found by experiment that if a piece of straight stock is taken and a line drawn on it through the center, and this piece of stock then is bent and the lengths of the inside, center, and outside lines be measured, the outside line will lengthen considerably as the piece is bent. The inside line will shorten correspondingly, while the center line will remain comparatively unaltered in length. This is universally true, and the proper length of stock required for making any bent shape may always be obtained by measuring the center line of the curve or bend. To return to the first example: In this case, if the center line of the stock be measured, $7\frac{1}{2}$ inches will be the length for each leg, thus making a total of 15 inches of stock required to make that particular bend. This is a universal rule which should always be followed when measuring stock, to take the length of the center line.

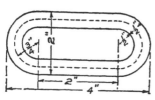

Fig. 55. Diagram for Calculating Stock in Link

Circles. On circles and parts of circles the length of stock may be easily calculated. The circumference, or distance around a circle, is found by multiplying the diameter by $3\frac{1}{7}$ or, more accurately, 3.1416. As an illustration, the stock necessary to bend up the ring in Fig. 54, would be calculated as follows: The inside diameter of the ring is 6 inches and the stock is 1 inch thick. This would make 7 inches the diameter C of the circle made by the center line, which may be called the calculating diameter, and the length of stock required would be $7 \times 3\frac{1}{7}$ or 22 inches.

Links. A combination of circle and straight lines is illustrated in Fig. 55. This link may be divided into two semicircles at the end, with two straight pieces at the sides. The outside diameter of the ends being 2 inches, would leave the straight sides each 2 inches long. The calculating diameter for the ends would be $1\frac{1}{2}$ inches. The total length of stock then required for the ends would be $1\frac{1}{2} \times 3\frac{1}{7} = 4\frac{5}{7}$, or approximately $4\frac{11}{16}$ inches. As each of the straight sides would take 2 inches of stock, the total length required would be $4 + 4\frac{11}{16} = 8\frac{11}{16}$ inches. With a slight allowance for welding, the amount cut should be $8\frac{3}{4}$ inches.

Fig. 56. Measuring Wheel

Measuring Wheel. Another method of measuring stock is by using a measuring wheel such as is shown in Fig. 56. This is simply a light running wheel mounted on a handle with some sort of a pointer attached. The wheel is sometimes made with a circumference of 24 inches and the rim graduated in inches and eighths. To use it, the wheel is placed lightly in contact with the line or object which it is wished to measure, with the zero mark on the wheel corresponding to the point from which the measurement is started. The wheel is then pushed along the surface following the line to be measured, with just enough pressure to cause it to revolve. By counting the revolutions and parts of a revolution made by the wheel, the required distance may be easily measured.

Measurement by String or Wire. *Scrolls and Irregular Shapes.* Difficult shapes may be measured by either of two methods. The commoner way is to lay the scroll or shape off full size and measure the length by laying on this full-sized drawing a string or thin piece of wire, causing the string or wire to follow the center line of the bent stock. The wire or string is then straightened and the length measured. This is about the easiest and best way of measuring work of this character.

Measurement by Dividers. Another method, which is more practical in the drafting room, consists of using a pair of dividers. The points of the dividers are set fairly close together and the center line is then stepped off and the number of steps counted. The same number of spaces are then laid off along a straight line and the length measured.

Bend Types

Ring and Eye Bending. In making a ring or an eye, the first step of course is to calculate the amount of stock required. In making ordinary rings 4 or 5 inches in diameter, the stock should be heated for about half its length. In starting the bend, the extreme end of the piece is first bent by placing the bar across

Fig. 57. Starting   Fig. 58. Finishing
        Eye Bend   Eye Bend

the horn of the anvil and bending it down as illustrated in Fig. 57. The bar is then pushed ahead and bent down as it is fed forward. The blows should not come directly on top of the horn but should fall outside of the point of support, as illustrated. This bends the iron and does not hammer it out of shape. One half of the circle is bent in this way, then the stock is turned end for end, the other end heated, and the second half bent in the same way as the first, the bending being started from the end as before.

Eye bending is done in a somewhat different manner. Suppose it be required to bend up an eye as shown in Fig. 58. To calculate the amount of stock required: The diameter in this case to be used is 2 inches, and the amount of stock required 2 inch$\times 3\frac{1}{7}$ inch = $6\frac{2}{7}$ inches, or practically $6\frac{3}{8}$ inches. This distance is laid off by making a chalk mark on the anvil $6\frac{3}{8}$ inches from the end. The iron is

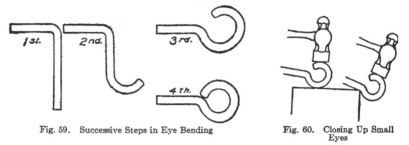

Fig. 59.　Successive Steps in Eye Bending

Fig. 60.　Closing Up Small Eyes

heated and placed against the anvil with one end on the chalk mark and the other end extending over the end of the anvil. The hand hammer is then held on the bar with one edge at the edge of the anvil, thus measuring off the required distance on the bar. Still holding the hammer on the bar the piece is laid across the anvil, with the edge

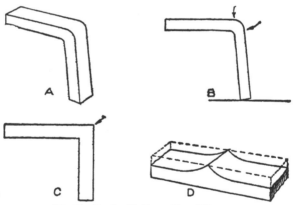

Fig. 61.　Bends with Square-Forged Corners

of the hammer even with the edge of the anvil and the $6\frac{3}{8}$ inches extending over the edge or corner. This piece is then bent down into a right angle as shown in the first illustration of Fig. 59. The eye is bent in much the same manner as the ring, except that all the bending is done from one end, the successive steps being shown in the illustration. Small eyes are closed up in the manner shown in Fig. 60.

Bend with Square=Forged Corner. *Upsetting.* Brackets and other forgings are frequently made with the outside corner square and sharp, as shown at *C*, Fig. 61, and, of the two ways of doing this, one method is to use the size of stock required for the sides, first shaping the corner as at *A*. This corner is then squared by upsetting the metal at the bend, the blows coming as shown by the arrows at *B*. The work should rest on the anvil face, and not over one corner, while being hammered.

Drawing Down Large Stock. A second method is to use thicker stock and to draw out the ends, leaving a hump, shown at *D*, where the outside corner of the bend is to come. The dotted lines show the original shape of the bar; the solid lines the shape before bending. Sometimes stock of the size used in the first method is taken and is upset to form the ridge, in place of drawing out the heavier stock.

The first method is the one more commonly used on medium sized work.

Twisted Gate Hook. It should be understood that the description given here will serve not only as a description of the particular

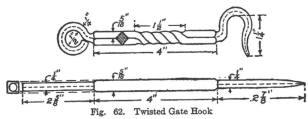

Fig. 62.   Twisted Gate Hook

piece in question but also as a general description of a variety of similarly shaped forgings. The methods used may be employed on other forgings of the same general shape.

Fig. 62 shows a twisted gate hook. To start with, it is necessary to determine exactly what lengths the different parts of the hook will have after they are forged to dimensions, and before they are bent to shape. Before bending, the work is first drawn down to size as is indicated in the illustration. The bar is left square in the center for the central part, and each end is drawn to $\frac{1}{4}$ inch round to form the hook and eye ends. The length of stock after being drawn out to $\frac{1}{4}$ inch round, required to make the eye, is $2\frac{3}{8}$ inches. Allowing about $\frac{1}{4}$ inch for the straight part before the eye is reached would make the total amount of stock required for the eye $2\frac{5}{8}$ inches. To

obtain the amount of stock for the hook it is necessary to lay off
the hook full size.   If the drawing is full-sized, the measuring may
be done directly on the drawing, but if not, a rough sketch having
the proper dimensions should be laid off and the measuring done
on that, the measuring of course being done along the dotted center
line.   This measuring is done by simply laying a string on the dotted
line, then straightening out the string and measuring its length.
In this way it will be found that $2\frac{7}{8}$ inches is required by the
hook.   The first step is then to forge the work into the shape shown
in Fig. 62.

Forming Shoulders.   The shoulder where the round stock
joins the square should be forged in the manner indicated in Fig. 63.
The bar is laid across the anvil with the point where the shoulder
is wished lying directly on the corner of the anvil.   The set hammer
is then placed on top of the work in such a way that the edge of the

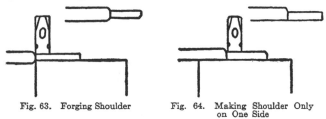

Fig. 63. Forging Shoulder   Fig. 64. Making Shoulder Only
                                              on One Side

set hammer comes directly in line with the edge of the anvil.   The
set hammer is then driven into the work with a sledge hammer.
The bar should be turned continually or an uneven shoulder will
be the result.   If a shoulder is wanted on one side only, as illustrated
in Fig. 64, it should be worked in as indicated there; that is, one
side of the iron should lie flat on the anvil face while the set hammer
works down the metal next to the shoulder.

After the two ends of the hook are drawn out, the eye and the
hook are bent up into shape.   The twist in the center of the hook
may be made either by using two pairs of tongs or by twisting in
a vise.   By the latter method a mark is first made on the vise in
such a way that, when the end of the hook is placed even with the
mark, the edge of the vise will come at the end of the point where
the twist is wanted.   The hook should be heated and placed in the
vise, the other end being grasped by a pair of tongs in such a way
that the distance between the tongs and the vise is just equal in

length to the twist. The twist is made by simply revolving the tongs around. In making a twist of this kind, no allowance need be made in length, as it practically has no effect on the length of the stock.

Eye Bolts. Eye bolts are made by two general methods, being either solid or welded. The solid eye bolt is much stronger. A solid eye bolt, or forged eye, as it is sometimes called, may be started in the general manner illustrated in Fig. 65. A nick is made on either side of a flat bar

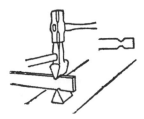

Fig. 65. Starting Solid Eye Bolt

by using top and bottom fullers as illustrated. The end is then rounded up as shown in Fig. 66. Particular attention should be given to seeing that the eye is forged as nearly to a perfect circle as possible before any punching is done. The stock around the eye is rounded up over the horn of the anvil as at *A*, by swinging it back and forth as it is hammered. The hole when first punched is like *B*, but when finished should be like *C*. The other end of the bar is then drawn down to form the round shank. If a very

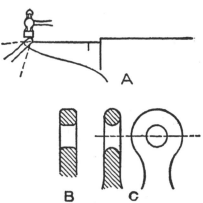

Fig. 66. Rounding Up Solid Eye Bolt

long shank is wanted a short stub shank may be formed in forging the eye and a round bar of the proper size welded on.

Welded eye bolts may be made in two different ways. The easier method produces an eye shaped as in Fig. 67. To make such a bolt, first scarf the end so that it will fit over the bend of the rod along the dotted line *ab*. Bend the eye over the horn of the anvil. Finally

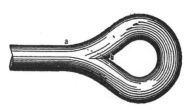

Fig. 67. Welded Eye Bolt

bring to a welding heat and weld in accordance with instructions already given.

An eye of better appearance, as shown in Fig. 68, is made as follows: Upset the body of the metal as a seat for the scarf at the end, as shown at *a*. Scarf the end of the bar and bend over the

Fig. 68.   Eye Bolt of Somewhat Better Form than Fig. 67

horn of the anvil into a true circle to fit the seat at *a*, and then weld as before.

The length of metal required for an eye or ring is nearly equal to the length of the circumference of a circle whose diameter is equal to the mean diameter of the ring.   Thus in Fig. 68 the length required for the eye will be approximately the length of the circle $abcb$ whose diameter is ac.

Chain Hooks.   These are made in a variety of shapes and with solid or welded eyes, the general method of making the eyes being

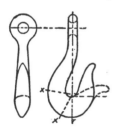

Fig. 69.   Chain Hook

exactly as described before under Eye Bolts. A common shape is shown in Fig. 69.   The stock is forged into shape similar to Fig. 70 before being bent.   To determine the length A the drawing is measured in the same way as described in making the gate hook.   The weakest point in most hooks is the part lying between the lines marked xx in Fig. 69.   This part of the hook should be heavier and stronger than the other parts.   When a strain is put on the hook, there is always a tendency to straighten out or to assume the shape shown by the dotted lines.

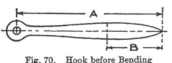

Fig. 70.   Hook before Bending

When forging the hook into shape, the dimension B, Fig. 70, should be made such that the heaviest part of the hook comes in this weakest point. After the hook is entirely forged to size, it should be bent into shape.   Hooks are also made from round and from square iron.   When made for hooking over a link, and so

TABLE I
Sizes of Hoisting Hooks

Item	Symbol	Sizes											
Load (tons)	T	$\frac{1}{8}$	$\frac{1}{4}$	$\frac{1}{2}$	1	$1\frac{1}{2}$	2	3	4	5	6	8	10
Stock (inches)	A	$\frac{5}{8}$	$1\frac{1}{16}$	$\frac{3}{4}$	$1\frac{1}{16}$	$1\frac{1}{4}$	$1\frac{3}{8}$	$1\frac{3}{4}$	2	$2\frac{1}{4}$	$2\frac{1}{2}$	$2\frac{7}{8}$	$3\frac{1}{4}$

shaped that the throat or opening is just large enough to slip
easily over a link edgewise, but too narrow to slip off of this link
down to the one which, of course, is turned at right angles, the
hook is known as a *grab hook*.

Hoisting Hooks. *Sizes.* A
widely accepted shape for hooks of
this character used on cranes is
shown in Fig. 71. The shape and
formulas for the dimensions are
given by Henry R. Towne in his
"Treatise on Cranes". The size of
stock required for a hook to carry any
particular load is given in Table I;
the load for which the hook is de-
signed being given in the upper line,
while the lower line gives the size
of the stock to be used in making
the hook.

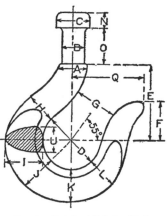

Fig. 71.   Details of Hoisting Hook

T = working load (tons of 2,000 pounds)

A = diameter (inches) of round stock used to form hook

The other dimensions of the hook are found by the following
formulas, all of the dimensions being given in inches:

$$B = .8 \quad A \qquad\qquad H = 1.08 \quad A$$
$$C = 1.2 \quad A \qquad\qquad I = 1.33 \quad A$$
$$D = .5 \quad T + 1.25 \qquad J = 1.2 \quad A$$
$$E = .64 \quad T + 1.6 \qquad K = 1.13 \quad A$$
$$F = .33 \quad T + .85 \qquad L = 1.05 \quad A$$
$$G = .75 \quad D \qquad\qquad M = .5 \quad A$$
$$O = .363 \ T + .66 \qquad N = .85 \quad B - .16$$
$$Q = .64 \quad T + 1.6 \qquad U = .866 A$$

Illustrative Example.   To illustrate the use of the table, suppose
it be required to make a hook to raise a load of 500 pounds or one-

quarter of a ton. In the line marked T is found the load $\frac{1}{4}$; directly below it are the figures $\frac{1}{1}\frac{1}{8}$, showing the size of stock to be used. The dimensions of the hook are found as follows:

$$D = .5 \times \frac{1}{4} + 1.25 = 1\frac{3}{8} \text{ inches}$$
$$E = .64 \times \frac{1}{4} + 1.6 = 1\frac{3}{4} \text{ inches (about)}$$
$$\text{Etc.}$$
$$I = 1.33 \ A = 1.33 \times \frac{1}{1}\frac{1}{8} = .915, \text{ or about } \frac{2}{3}\frac{9}{2} \text{ inch}$$

When reducing the decimals the dimensions which have to do only with the bending of the hook, i.e., the opening, length, length of point, etc., may be taken to the nearest 16th, but the dimensions through the body of the hook or stock should be reduced to the nearest 32nd on small hooks. The completed dimensions of the hook in question, of 500-pound capacity, would be as follows:

$D = 1\frac{3}{8}$ inches	$I = \frac{29}{32}$ inch
$E = 1\frac{3}{4}$ inches	$J = \frac{13}{16}$ inch
$F = \frac{13}{16}$ inch	$K = \frac{25}{32}$ inch
$G = 1$ inch	$L = \frac{23}{32}$ inch
$O = \frac{3}{4}$ inch	$M = \frac{11}{32}$ inch
$Q = 1\frac{3}{4}$ inches	$U = \frac{13}{32}$ inch
$H = \frac{3}{4}$ inch	

Bolts. *Upset-Head Types.* Of the two methods of making bolts, either by upsetting or by welding the heads, the first method

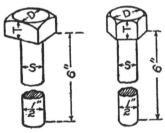

Fig. 72. Bolts with Square and Hexagon Heads

is more common on small bolts and machine made bolts. The welded head is more commonly used for heavy hand forged bolts. The upset head is the stronger provided both are equally well made. The size of the bolt is always given as the diameter and length of shank or stem. Thus a bolt known as $\frac{1}{2}$-inch by 6-inch, or $\frac{1}{2}$-inch bolt 6 inches long, would mean a bolt having a shank $\frac{1}{2}$ inch in diameter and 6 inches long from the under side of the head to the end of the stem, having the dimensions of the bolt shown in Fig. 72. The dimensions of the bolt heads are always the same for the same sized bolt, and are determined from the diameter of the shank. The diameter of the head at D, Fig. 72, is the distance across the head from flat side to flat side, and is known as the *diameter across the flats*. The thickness of the head is taken as shown at T. If S equals the diameter of the shank of the bolt, the dimensions of the head would be as follows:

$$D = 1\tfrac{1}{2} \times S + \tfrac{1}{8} \text{ inch}$$
$$T = S$$

For a two-inch bolt the dimensions would be as follows:

Diameter of head $D = 1\tfrac{1}{2} \times 2 + \tfrac{1}{8} = 3\tfrac{1}{8}$ inches

The thickness of head T would be equal to diameter of the shank, or 2 inches. These dimensions are for rough or unfinished heads. Each dimension of a finished head is $\tfrac{1}{16}$ inch less than the same dimension of a rough head. Bolts generally have the top corners of the head rounded or chamfered off. This may be done with a hand hammer; or with a cupping tool, which is simply a set hammer with the bottom face hollowed out into a cup shape.

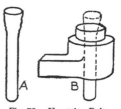

Fig. 73. Upsetting Bolt Heads

Where large quantities of bolts are to be made, the bars are heated in a furnace and headed by special machinery. Where the work is done by hand the tools are of the simplest character. The method of upsetting is shown in Fig. 73. The header consists of a disc in which a hole has been drilled to correspond to the diameter of the bolt. A handle 12 or 15 inches in length is welded to the disc. Such a tool is shown in Fig. 74. The hole should be about $\tfrac{1}{32}$ inch larger than the nominal size of iron. To make a bolt with this tool: First cut off the iron to the required length; then heat the end to be headed, to a dull straw color; strike the end with a hammer or against the anvil and upset it so that the portion

Fig. 74. Typical Bolt Header

intended for the formation of the head will not pass through the header. Then place the hole of the header over the square hole in the tail of the anvil and drop the cold end of the bolt through it.

Strike the projecting portion of the bar and upset it until the requisite thickness of head is obtained. This will probably leave a head of curved but irregular outline. Remove from the header and square the head thus upset, on the face of the anvil. This will probably thicken the head. Again drop the cold end through the header and strike the head until it is reduced to proper thickness. After which, again square the edges on the face of the anvil. In doing this work, the smith will hold the header in his left hand. The work will be facilitated if a helper assists with a sledge hammer.

There are a number of simple tools in use for clamping the bar while it is being headed so as to avoid the preliminary upsetting.

Welded-Head Type. Bolts of this type are made by welding a ring of square iron around the end of the shank to form the head.

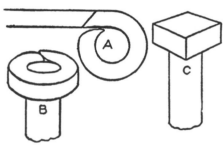

Fig. 75. Welded-Head Bolt

The ring is generally bent up on the end of a bar as shown at *A*, Fig. 75, but not welded. This ring is cut off and placed on the end of the shank as shown at *B*. The joint in the ring should be left slightly open to allow for the expansion in welding. The ring is fastened to the end of the shank by striking it on one side and squeezing it against the shank. The bolt is put into the fire, heated to the welding heat, and the head welded up into the required shape. The ring should not be welded round at first, as it is difficult in this way to make a sound joint, there being a much better chance of doing sound work by welding the head directly square or hexagonal as required. No attention need be paid to the joint in the ring as this will take care of itself. Considerable care must be used in taking the welding heat, as all the heat which reaches the joint must pass through the ring and there is a good chance of burning the ring before the shank reaches the welding heat if the heating is not done slowly and carefully.

Tongs. Common flat-jawed tongs, such as are used for holding light work, may be made as follows: The stock should be about 1 inch by ¾ inch. The first step should be to work the stock down over the edge of the anvil, as shown at *A*, Fig. 76. Turn the flat side at an angle of about 45 degrees on anvil as shown at *B*, and work down to half the thickness of the jaw hammered out.   Then work down the stock on the round horn of the anvil, as shown at *C*.   Then

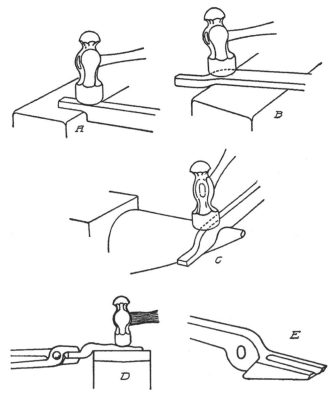

Fig. 76.   Steps in Making Flat-Jawed Tongs

draw out the handle, as shown at *D*, allowing enough stock to work out the proper length; or a small amount of stock may be taken, a short stub drawn out, and the round stock welded on, making the proper length as shown in Fig. 77.   The last step is to punch the hole for the rivet.   It is always a good plan to slightly increase the inside face of the jaw with a fuller, as shown at *E*, Fig. 76,

Fig. 77.   Welding-On Round Stock

as this insures the jaws gripping the work firmly with the edges, and not touching it simply at one point in the center, as they sometimes do if this crease is not made.   The tongs are then riveted together, the riveting being done with the round end of the hammer; in this way a head is formed on the rivet without upsetting the shank of the rivet very much where it passes through the hole. After riveting, the

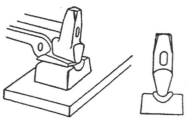

Fig. 78.   Method of Making Jaws for Round-Nose Tongs

tongs will probably be stiff or hard to move. They may be loosened up by heating the eye part red hot and moving the handles forward and backward two or three times. They should then be firmly fitted to the work to be handled.

Tongs for Round Stock. Tongs for handling round stock may be made by the general method described above, the only difference being that after the jaws are shaped, and before riveting together, they should be rounded up as illustrated in Fig. 78, using a fuller and swage as shown.

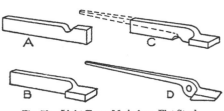

Fig. 79.   Light Tongs Made from Flat Stock

Light Tongs. Light tongs may be made from flat stock in the manner illustrated in Fig. 79. With a fuller, a cut is made near one end in a piece of flat stock, as at *A*. This end is twisted over at right

angles as shown at *B*. Another cut is made on the opposite side, as at *C*, and the end drawn out as indicated by the dotted lines. The tongs are then finished in the usual way. Tongs of this character may be used for very light work and are easily made.

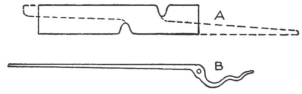

Fig. 80.   Method of Forging Pick-Up Tongs

Pick-Up Tongs. Pick-up tongs are made in much the same way as described above, the different steps being illustrated in Fig. 80.

Bolt Tongs. Bolt tongs may be made from round stock, although square may be sometimes used to advantage. The first step is to bend the bar in the shape shown in Fig. 81, which may be

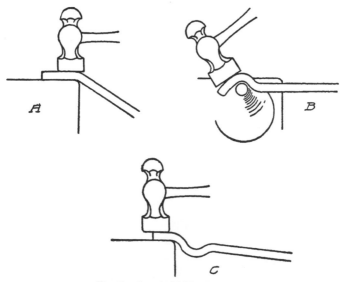

Fig. 81. Steps in Making Bolt Tongs

done by the hammer at the edge of the anvil, shown at *A*, and on the anvil horn as at *B*. The jaw proper is rounded and finished as shown at *C*. The part between the jaw proper and the eye may be worked down into shape by the fuller and set hammer. The finishing may be done as indicated in Fig. 82. The eye and handle are then flattened down and drawn out, the tongs are punched, riveted together, finished, and fitted in the usual manner.

Fig. 82. Finishing Bolt Tongs

Ladles. Ladles similar to the one shown in Fig. 83, may be made from two pieces welded together, one forming the handle, the other the bowl, or as sometimes is done, the handle may be riveted on. A piece of flat stock is first "laid out" as shown in

Fig. 84. This is then cut out with a cold chisel and the handle is welded on at the projecting point. In forming the bowl the stock

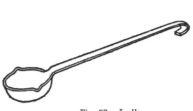

Fig. 83. Ladle

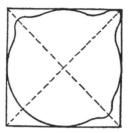

Fig. 84. Flat Stock for Ladle

is heated evenly and placed over a round hole in a swage block or other object—a hole being chosen which is slightly smaller

Fig. 85. Method of Rounding Ladle Bowl

than the outside diameter of the piece to be worked—and to

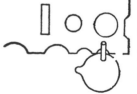

Fig. 86. Forming Ladle Lips

round the bowl it is worked as indicated in Fig. 85, with the peen end of the hammer. The forming should be done as much as possible by working near the edge of the piece rather than in the center. After the bowl has been properly shaped the edges should be ground off smooth and the lips formed as shown in Fig. 86. This is done by placing the part from which the lip is made against one of the small grooves in the side of the swage block and driving in a piece of small round iron, thus hollowing out the lip. The stock draws in somewhat when being rounded up. For the bowl of a ladle 3½ inches in diameter, the stock when flat should have an outside diameter of about 4 inches, and be ⅛ inch thick. Machine steel should be used for making the bowl; if ordinary wrought iron is used, the metal is almost sure to split.

MEDIUM FORGED WORK

Calculation of Stock

Stock Changed in Shape. The calculations made previously for stock, were for stock which was simply bent into shape, the original section or size of the stock remaining unaltered. There is a large variety of work where the shape of the stock is considerably changed, and where it is essential to know the amount

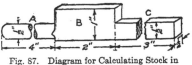

Fig. 87.   Diagram for Calculating Stock in Special Forging

required to make a given forging. In doing this kind of work one rule must be remembered, i.e., that the volume of the stock remains unaltered although its shape may be changed. Take as an example the forging shown in Fig. 87, let us determine the amount of stock required to make the piece.

The forging is made in the general manner shown in Fig. 88. A piece of stock should be taken large enough in section to make the block *B*, Fig. 87, which will mean that it will be 1 inch wide and ½ inch thick. The metal is worked by making the fuller cuts, as shown in Fig. 88, and then drawing down the ends to the required size, it being, of

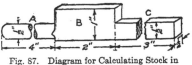

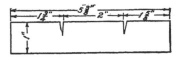

Fig. 88.   Steps in Making Forging

course, necessary to know the amount of stock required for each end.

For convenience in calculating, the forging will be divided into three parts, the rounded end *A*, the central rectangular block *B*, and the square end *C*, Fig. 87. The stock used being 1 inch by ½ inch, the block *B* will of course require just 2 inches of stock. The end C would have a volume of $\frac{1}{2}\times\frac{1}{2}\times3=\frac{3}{4}$ cubic inch. The stock has a volume of $\frac{1}{2}\times1\times1=\frac{1}{2}$ cubic inch for each inch of length. The number of inches of stock required for the end C would then be $\frac{3}{4}\div\frac{1}{2}$, or $1\frac{1}{2}$ inches. The end A is a round shaft or cylinder 4 inches long and $\frac{1}{2}$ inch in diameter. To find the volume of a cylinder, multiply the square of the radius ($\frac{1}{2}$ the diameter) by $3\frac{1}{7}$ and then multiply this result by the length of the cylinder. This will give the volume of A as $\frac{1}{4}\times\frac{1}{4}\times3\frac{1}{7}\times4=\frac{1}{1}\frac{1}{4}$, and the amount of stock required to make this piece would be $1\frac{1}{1}\frac{1}{4}\div\frac{1}{2}=1\frac{4}{7}$, which may be taken as $1\frac{5}{8}$ inches. There is, of course, some slight loss due to scaling in working the iron, which must be allowed for. This is generally done by adding a slight amount to the minimum amount required in each case. The amount of stock required in this case would be about

Round shaft A	$1\frac{3}{4}$ inches
Block B	2 inches
Square shaft C	$1\frac{3}{8}$ inches
Total	$5\frac{3}{8}$ inches

When the forging is started, cuts, which are afterward opened up with a fuller, may be made as shown by the upper sketch in

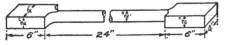

Fig. 88. In this particular case it is not absolutely necessary that exactly the proper amount of stock be taken, as

Fig. 89. Diagram of Connecting Rod

it would be a very easy matter to take a little too much and trim off the surplus from the ends, after the forging was made.

With the forging such as shown in Fig. 89, however, it is essential that the exact amount be used. This forging, which is the general shape of a connecting rod, would be started as shown in Fig. 90, and it is quite important that the distance A be correct.

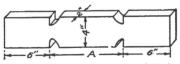

The stock used should be 2 inches by 4 inches. Each end will, of course, require just 6 inches of stock. The center part is a cylinder 2 inches in diameter and 24 inches

Fig. 90. Starting Connecting-Rod Work

long, the volume of which would be $1\times1\times3\frac{1}{7}\times24=75\frac{3}{7}$ cubic inches, which may be taken as $75\frac{1}{2}$ cubic inches. For each inch in length the 2-inch by 4-inch stock would have a volume of

TABLE II

Weight of Flat Rolled Iron

(LENGTH 12 INCHES)

Thickness	½	⅝	¾	⅞	1	1⅛	1¼	1⅜	1½	1⅝	1¾	1⅞	2	2⅛	2¼	2⅜	2½	2⅝	2¾	2⅞	3
	.208	.260	.313	.365	.417	.469	.521	.573	.625	.677	.729	.781	.833	.885	.938	.989	1.04	1.09	1.15	1.20	1.25
	.416	.521	.625	.729	.833	.938	1.04	1.15	1.25	1.35	1.46	1.56	1.67	1.77	1.88	1.98	2.08	2.18	2.29	2.39	2.50
	.624	.781	.938	1.09	1.25	1.41	1.56	1.72	1.88	2.03	2.19	2.35	2.50	2.65	2.81	2.97	3.13	3.28	3.44	3.59	3.75
	.833	1.04	1.25	1.46	1.67	1.88	2.08	2.29	2.50	2.71	2.92	3.13	3.33	3.54	3.75	3.96	4.17	4.37	4.58	4.79	5.00
		1.30	1.56	1.82	2.08	2.35	2.60	2.86	3.13	3.39	3.65	3.91	4.17	4.43	4.69	4.95	5.21	5.47	5.73	5.99	6.25
			1.88	2.19	2.50	2.81	3.13	3.44	3.75	4.06	4.38	4.69	5.00	5.31	5.63	5.94	6.25	6.56	6.88	7.19	7.50
				2.55	2.92	3.28	3.65	4.01	4.38	4.74	5.10	5.46	5.83	6.19	6.57	6.92	7.29	7.65	8.02	8.38	8.75
					3.33	3.75	4.17	4.58	5.00	5.42	5.83	6.25	6.67	7.08	7.50	7.91	8.33	8.75	9.17	9.58	10.00
						4.22	4.69	5.15	5.63	6.09	6.56	7.03	7.50	7.97	8.44	8.90	9.38	9.84	10.31	10.78	11.25
							5.21	5.73	6.25	6.77	7.29	7.81	8.33	8.85	9.38	9.89	10.42	10.94	11.46	11.98	12.50
								6.30	6.88	7.45	8.02	8.59	9.17	9.74	10.32	10.88	11.46	12.03	12.60	13.17	13.75
									7.50	8.12	8.75	9.37	10.00	10.62	11.25	11.87	12.50	13.12	13.75	14.37	15.00
										8.80	9.45	10.14	10.83	11.51	12.19	12.86	13.54	14.22	14.90	15.57	16.25
											10.21	10.94	11.67	12.40	13.13	13.85	14.58	15.31	16.04	16.77	17.50
												11.72	12.50	13.28	14.06	14.84	15.63	16.41	17.19	17.97	18.75
													13.33	14.16	15.00	15.83	16.67	17.50	18.33	19.16	20.00
														15.05	15.94	16.81	17.71	18.59	19.48	20.36	21.25
															16.88	17.80	18.75	19.69	20.63	21.56	22.50
																18.80	19.79	20.78	21.78	22.76	23.75
																	20.83	21.87	22.93	23.96	25.00
																		22.97	24.07	25.16	26.25
																			25.21	26.35	27.50
																				27.55	28.75
																					30.00

$4\times2\times1=8$ cubic inches. Therefore it would require $75\frac{1}{2}\div8=9\frac{7}{16}$ inches of stock, to form the central piece, consequently the distance between the cuts shown at A in Fig. 90, will be $9\frac{7}{16}$ inches. To this might be added a slight allowance for loss in scaling. The total amount of stock required would be $6+6+9\frac{7}{16}=21\frac{7}{16}$ inches. Any forging may generally be separated into simple parts of uniform shape as was done above. In this form the calculation may be easily made.

Weight of Forging. To find the weight of any forging the volume may first be found in cubic inches and this multiplied by .2779, the weight of wrought iron per cubic inch. If the forging be made of steel, the figures .2835 should be used in place of .2779. This gives the weight in pounds. Below is given the weight of wrought iron, cast iron, and steel, both in pounds per cubic inch and per cubic foot.

Cast iron	450 per cu. ft.	.2604 per cu. inch
Wrought iron	480 per cu. ft.	.2779 per cu. inch
Steel	490 per cu. ft.	.2835 per cu. inch

Suppose it were required to find the weight of the forging shown in Fig. 87. A has a volume of $1\frac{1}{4}$ cubic inch, C $\frac{3}{4}$ cubic inch, and B 1 cubic inch, making a total of $2\frac{1}{2}\frac{5}{8}$ cubic inches. If the forging were made of wrought iron it would weigh $2\frac{1}{2}\frac{5}{8}\times.2779=.7$ pound. The forging in Fig. 89 has a total volume of $171\frac{3}{4}$ cubic inches and would weigh, if made of wrought iron, 47.64 pounds.

A much easier way to calculate weights is to use tables such as II and III given herewith. Table II gives the weights per foot of flat iron bars. In Table III is given the weights for each foot of length of round and square bars.

When using Table II to ascertain the weight of any size of flat iron per foot of length, look in the first column at the left for the thickness. Then follow out in a horizontal line to the column giving the width. The number given will be the weight in pounds of one foot of the desired size.

To use the table for calculating weights, the procedure would be as follows:

Taking Fig. 89 as an example, each end is 2 inches by 4 inches and 6 inches long, and, as far as the weight is concerned, the two ends would be equal to a bar 2 inches by 4 inches and 1 foot long. From the table it will be seen that a bar 2 inches by 2 inches weighs 13.33 pounds, and a bar 2 inches by 4 inches, being twice as thick would weigh twice that, or 26.66 pounds. A bar 2 inches in diameter weighs 10.47 pounds per foot and, as the central part of the forging is 2 feet long, it will weigh 20.94 pounds, making the total weight of the forging 47.6 pounds.

Finish. Many forgings are machined or finished after leaving the forge shop. The drawings are always made to represent the

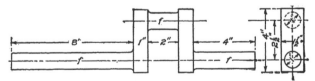

Fig. 91. Finished Single-Throw Crank Shaft

finished work and therefore give the finished dimensions, and it is necessary when this finishing is to be done, to make allowance for it when making the forging, that all parts which have to be finished or machined may be left with an extra metal to be removed in

TABLE III

Weights of Round and Square Rolled Iron

(Length 12 Inches)

Thickness (in.)	Weight (lb.) Square	Round	Thickness (in.)	Weight (lb.) Square	Round	Thickness (in.)	Weight (lb.) Square	Round
0			1 11/16	24.08	18.91	5 3/8	96.30	75.64
1/16	.013	.010	2/4	25.21	19.80	5 7/16	98.55	77.40
1/8	.052	.041	1 13/16	26.37	20.71	5 1/2	100.8	79.19
3/16	.117	.092	7/8	27.55	21.64	5 9/16	103.1	81.00
1/4	.208	.164	1 15/16	28.76	22.59	5 5/8	105.5	82.83
5/16	.326	.256	3	30.00	23.56	5 11/16	107.8	84.69
3/8	.469	.368	1/16	31.26	24.55	5 3/4	110.2	86.56
7/16	.638	.501	1/8	32.55	25.57	5 13/16	112.6	88.45
1/2	.833	.654	3/16	33.87	26.60	5 7/8	115.1	90.36
9/16	1.055	.828	1/4	35.21	27.65	5 15/16	117.5	92.29
5/8	1.302	1.023	5/16	36.58	28.73	6	120.0	94.25
11/16	1.576	1.237	3/8	37.97	29.82	1/8	125.1	98.22
3/4	1.875	1.473	7/16	39.39	30.94	1/4	130.2	102.3
13/16	2.201	1.728	1/2	40.83	32.07	3/8	135.5	106.4
7/8	2.552	2.004	9/16	42.30	33.23	1/2	140.8	110.6
15/16	2.930	2.301	5/8	43.80	34.40	5/8	146.3	114.9
1	3.333	2.618	11/16	45.33	35.60	3/4	151.9	119.3
1/16	3.763	2.955	3/4	46.88	36.82	7/8	157.6	123.7
1/8	4.219	3.313	13/16	48.45	38.05	7	163.3	128.3
3/16	4.701	3.692	7/8	50.05	39.31	1/8	169.2	132.9
1/4	5.208	4.091	15/16	51.68	40.59	1/4	175.2	137.6
5/16	5.742	4.510	4	53.33	41.89	3/8	181.3	142.4
3/8	6.302	4.950	1/16	55.01	43.21	1/2	187.5	147.3
7/16	6.888	5.410	1/8	56.72	44.55	5/8	193.8	152.2
1/2	7.500	5.890	3/16	58.45	45.91	3/4	200.2	157.2
9/16	8.138	6.392	1/4	60.21	47.29	7/8	206.7	162.4
5/8	8.802	6.913	5/16	61.99	48.69	8	213.3	167.6
11/16	9.492	7.455	3/8	63.80	50.11	1/4	226.9	178.2
3/4	10.21	8.018	7/16	65.64	51.55	1/2	240.8	189.2
13/16	10.95	8.601	1/2	67.50	53.01	3/4	255.2	200.4
7/8	11.72	9.204	9/16	69.39	54.50	9	270.0	212.1
15/16	12.51	9.828	5/8	71.30	56.00	1/4	285.2	224.0
2	13.33	10.47	11/16	73.24	57.52	1/2	300.8	236.3
1/16	14.18	11.14	3/4	75.21	59.07	3/4	316.9	248.9
1/8	15.05	11.82	13/16	77.20	60.63	10	333.3	261.3
3/16	15.95	12.53	7/8	79.22	62.22	1/4	350.2	275.1
1/4	16.88	13.25	15/16	81.26	63.82	1/2	367.5	288.6
5/16	17.83	14.00	5	83.33	65.45	3/4	385.2	302.5
3/8	18.80	14.77	1/16	85.43	67.10	11	403.3	316.8
7/16	19.80	15.55	1/8	87.55	68.76	1/4	421.9	331.3
1/2	20.83	16.36	3/16	89.70	70.45	1/2	440.8	346.2
9/16	21.89	17.19	1/4	91.88	72.16	3/4	460.2	361.4
5/8	22.97	18.04	5/16	94.08	73.89	12	480.	377.

finishing. The parts required to be finished are generally marked on the drawing. Sometimes the finished surfaces have the word *finished* marked on them. Sometimes the finishing is shown simply by the symbol f, as used in Fig. 91, showing that the shafts and pin only of the crank are to be finished. When all surfaces of a piece are to be finished the words *finish all over* are sometimes marked on the drawing.

The allowance for finishing on small forgings is generally about $\frac{1}{16}$ inch on each surface. Thus, if a block were wanted to finish 4 inches by 2 inches by 1 inch, and $\frac{1}{16}$ inch were allowed for finishing, the dimensions of the forging would be $4\frac{1}{8}$ inches by $2\frac{1}{8}$ inches by $1\frac{1}{8}$ inches. On a forging like Fig. 89, about $\frac{1}{8}$ inch allowance would be made for finishing, if it were called for. Thus the diameter of the central shaft would be $2\frac{1}{4}$ inches, the thickness of the ends $2\frac{1}{4}$ inches, etc. On larger work $\frac{1}{4}$ inch is sometimes allowed for machining. The amount of finish allowed depends to a large extent on the way the forging is to be finished. With hand finishing, that is, filing or scraping, $\frac{1}{32}$ inch or even $\frac{1}{64}$ inch is enough; when a lathe or other machine is used, more material should be left.

When a forging calls for finish, in calculating the amount of stock, or the weight, the dimensions taken should not be the actual ones shown by the drawing, but these dimensions with the proper allowance made for finish.

Standard Large Types

Crank Shafts. There are several methods of forging crank shafts. The one more commonly used is the commercial method, as described in detail below. When forgings were mostly made of wrought iron, the cranks were welded up of several pieces. One piece is used for each of the shafts, one piece for each cheek or side, and another piece for the crank pin. Cranks are sometimes bent up out of round stock, but this method is only used on small work.

Common Method of Making. The common method now employed where machine steel is used, is to forge the crank from

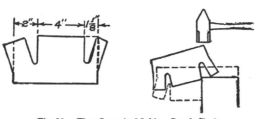

Fig. 92. First Steps in Making Crank Shaft

one solid piece of material. The stock is taken large enough to shape the largest part of the crank without any upsetting. If a crank is required similar to Fig. 91, the size of stock to be used should be $1\frac{1}{2}$ inches by 4 inches in section.

The first thing to do of course is to calculate the amount of stock required. The long end would contain 10.13 cubic inches. As each inch of stock contains 6 cubic inches, it would require 1.7 inches of stock to form this end, provided there was no waste from scale. Waste does take place, however, and must be allowed for, so about

2 inches of stock should be taken. The short end contains 5.22 cubic inches and would require 0.87 inch of stock, without allowance for scale. About $1\frac{1}{8}$ inches should be taken. The total stock then required would be $7\frac{1}{8}$ inches.

The first step is to make the cuts, and spread the ends as shown in Fig. 92. These ends may then be forged down with a sledge hammer, as illustrated, or may be worked out under the steam hammer, the finishing up against the shoulders being done as illustrated in Fig. 93. The shaft may be rounded down and finished between swages. Care must be taken to see

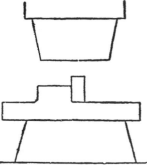

Fig. 93. Finishing Up Shoulder

that the cuts are properly spread before drawing out the ends. If the cuts are left without spreading, the metal acts somewhat after the manner shown in Fig. 94. The top part of the bar, as it is worked down, folds over and leaves a crack or cold-shut as illustrated. When the metal starts to act in this way the fault should be corrected by trimming off the overlapping corner along the dotted line shown in the upper sketch.

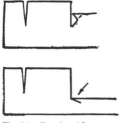

Fig. 94. Results of Improper Spreading

When the forging leaves the shop, it will be left in a shape similar to that shown by the solid lines in Fig. 95, the dimensions shown here allowing for the necessary finishing. The crank itself would be left in a solid block, the throat being afterwards cut out as indicated by the dotted lines. A line of holes is first drilled as shown,

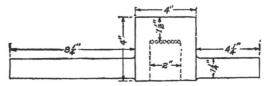

Fig. 95. Crank-Shaft Forging Ready for Machining

and the block of metal to be taken out is removed by making two slits with a cold saw and the block then knocked out with a sledge hammer. It is possible to form this throat by chopping out the surplus metal with a hot chisel in the forge shop, but on small cranks in particular, such as here shown, it is generally cheaper in a well equipped shop to use the first method.

Multiple-Throw Cranks. When a crank shaft has more than one crank or crank pin, it is spoken of as a multiple-throw crank; a

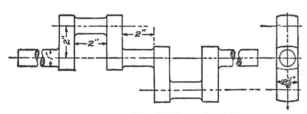

Fig. 96.   Finished Double-Throw Crank Shaft

double-throw crank is a crank shaft with two cranks; a three-throw or triple-throw, one with three cranks; etc. As a general rule, multiple-throw cranks are forged flat, i.e., the cranks are all forged in line with each other. The shafts and pins are then rough turned and the cranks are heated and twisted into shape. The forging for

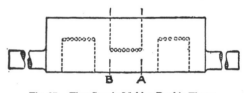

Fig. 97.   First Step in Making Double-Throw
Crank Shaft

the double-throw crank shown finished in Fig. 96 would first be made in the general shape shown in Fig. 97. The parts shown by the dotted lines would then be cut out with a drill and saw as described above, and the shafts and pins rough turned, i.e., turned round, but left as large as possible. The forging is then returned to the forge shop where it is heated and the cranks twisted to the desired angle. When twisting, the crank

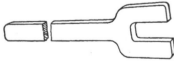

Fig. 98.   Wrench for Crank Twisting

would be gripped just to the right of the point marked *A*. This may be done with a vise, or a wrench if the crank is small, or it may be held under the steam hammer. The twisting may be done with a wrench similar to that shown in Fig. 98, which may be easily made by bending up a U of flat stock and welding on a handle.

Three-Throw Crank. A three-throw crank without any inter-

mediate bearings is shown in Fig. 99. The rough forging for this is
shown in Fig. 100. The extra metal is removed, as indicated by the
dotted lines, and the twisting is done as described before.

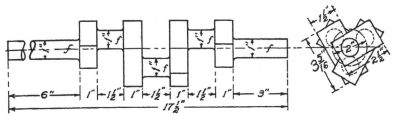

Fig. 99. Diagram of Finished Three-Throw Crank Shaft

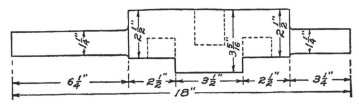

Fig. 100. Three-Throw Crank Forging Ready for Machining

Weldless Rings. Rings and eyes forged solid without any
welds may be made in the general manner described below. As an
example, suppose it be required to make a ring such as illustrated
in Fig. 101. It is necessary, of course, to calculate the amount of
stock required. This may be done as follows:
The first step is to determine the area of the
ring, which is done by taking the area of the outside circle, and subtracting from it the area of
the inside circle, as follows:

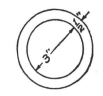

> Outside circle area 12.57 sq. in.
> Inside circle area 7.07 sq. in.
> Ring area   5.50 sq. in.

The stock used when making small thin
rings should be twice the width of the side of the
ring to which is added at least ¼ inch. A flat bar is

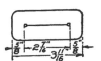

Fig. 101. Weldless
Ring

first forged rounding on the ends, punched and split as shown;
this split is opened out and the ring is hammered into shape.
When the bar is split the stock is more or less deformed and when

worked back into shape is slightly thinned. Although no stock is lost by the hammering, an allowance must be made for the thinning and stretching and it is necessary to make the stock slightly wider

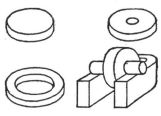

on this account, as noted above. Allowing $\frac{1}{2}$ inch for hammering, and taking stock $1\frac{1}{2}$ inches wide, the amount of stock required would be $5.5 \div 1.5$, equal to 3.66 inches. Allowing a small amount for loss by scale, etc., $3\frac{11}{16}$ inches of stock should be taken. In making this calculation, the thickness of the stock is not taken into consideration, as the thick-

Fig. 102. Weldless Ring Made under Steam Hammer

ness of the finished ring is the same as the stock. This general method is used on a large variety of work, particularly where rings are to be made of tool steel and should be made without a weld.

Another method of making weldless rings, under the steam hammer, is illustrated in Fig. 102. The proper amount of stock is first forged into a disc, a hole is punched into this disc and a mandrel inserted. A U-shaped rest is then placed on the anvil of the steam hammer and the mandrel laid on this. The ring is turned on the mandrel and forged into shape. Larger and larger mandrels are substituted as the hole in the ring increases in size.

Lever with Boss. Taking as an example the forging shown in Fig. 103, the following description will serve for many forgings of the same general shape. There are two general ways of making work of this character. One is to take stock of the proper size for the lever and to weld on a chunk for the boss. The other is to take stock large enough to form the boss and to draw out either the entire lever,

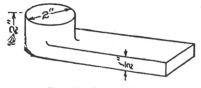

Fig. 103. Lever with Boss

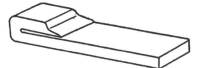

Fig. 104. Stock Bent for Forging Boss

or a short stub, to which the lever is welded. The work may be started for the first method by bending over the end of the stock as illustrated in Fig. 104. This is welded up and rounded by the same

general method as afterward described for the other boss. The
second method of shaping is illustrated in Fig. 105. The stock in
this case would be 2 inches square. The fuller cut is first made as
illustrated at *A*. The end is then drawn out into the shape shown at

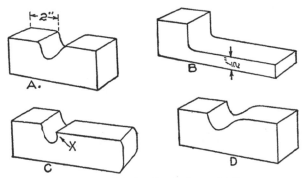

Fig. 105.   Method of Shaping Lever with Boss

B. In drawing out the stock, if the metal be allowed to flatten down
into shape like *C*, a cold-shut will be formed close to the boss, as the
corner at *X* will overlap and work into the metal, making a crack in
the work. The proper way to draw out the stock is shown at *D*.
The square piece left for the boss is rounded up over the corner of
the anvil as shown in Fig. 106. Sometimes to make the work easier

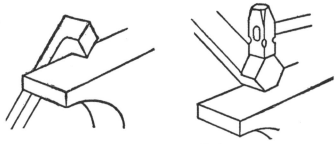

Fig. 106.   Rounding-Up Boss

to get at, the end is bent back out of the way and straightened after
the forging is completed. The boss may be smoothed up by using a
set hammer or swage in the manner indicated.

Knuckles. One example of a very numerous class of forgings is
shown in Fig. 107. This is the shape used for what are known as
marine ends of connecting rods, knuckle joints on valve rods, and

various other pieces.   A common method employed to make such a
forging is shown in Fig. 108.   Two fuller cuts are first made as

indicated at *A* and the part for the shaft of the
forging drawn out. The thick end is then punched
and split, as indicated at *B*.   This split end is
opened up and forged out in the manner indi-

Fig. 107.   Knuckle

cated in Fig. 109, if the work is done on the
anvil.   Fig. 110 illustrates the method of working out under the
steam hammer, the end being first flattened as indicated and then

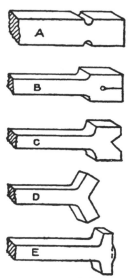

gradually tipped up to the position shown by
the dotted lines.   When drawn to size, the
ends are flattened out straight across and the
finishing done around the shank with a fuller,
as indicated in Fig. 111.   The forging is then
bent into a U-shaped loop of approximately
the shape of the finished knuckle.   A bar of
iron the same dimension as the inside of the
finished knuckle is inserted between the sides
of the loop, and the sides closed down flat, as
shown in Fig. 112. Fig. 113 shows other forgings which may be shaped by this same general method.   Trim *E*, Fig. 108, to the dotted line.

Wrenches. *S-Wrench.* A simple tool that
is frequently called for is the **S**-wrench. This

Fig. 108.   Method of Making
Knuckle

wrench is usually made with a gap at each
end suited for nuts of different sizes.   It is
shown complete in Fig. 114.   The jaws at
the end should be parallel with each other.
A line drawn from one pair of jaws to the
other should make an angle of 30 degrees
with the center line of each.   There are
two ways in which such a wrench can be
forged.   One is to forge the jaws separately
and then weld to the handle.   In the other
the jaws are cut from a solid piece of metal

Fig. 109.   Opening Up

and the iron between is then drawn down to the proper size for the
handle.   The latter is preferable, since it avoids all welds.

To make the wrench by the second process, select a piece of steel large enough to form the head. Fuller it down back of the head as shown in *A*, Fig. 115, at *a a*. Round the end and punch the hole *b*. Next treat the other end in the same way and draw out the inter-

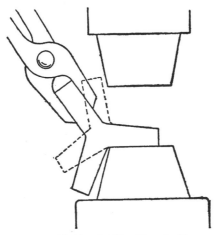

Fig. 110.　Working Out Knuckle under Steam
Hammer

mediate metal giving the form shown at *B*. Now cut out the holes *b b* securing the form shown at *C*. It now remains to bend the heads to the proper angle and to give the desired curve to the shank. In forging such a wrench the outer edges should be slightly rounded so

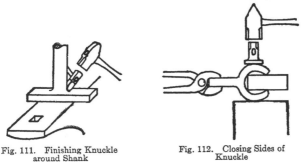

Fig. 111.　Finishing Knuckle
around Shank

Fig. 112.　Closing Sides of
Knuckle

that they will not cut the hand. The inside of the jaws should be perfectly square with the sharp edges; this finish can best be obtained by filing.

Socket Wrench. Socket wrenches are made in several ways. The easiest way in "hurry-up" work is the method illustrated in

Fig. 116. A stub is forged to the same size and shape as the finished hole is to be, and a ring, bent up of thin flat iron, welded around

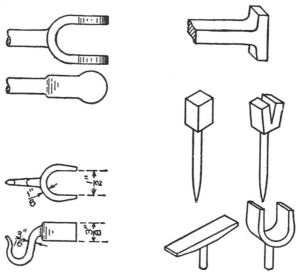

Fig. 113. Typical Shapes Similar to Knuckles

this stub. When finishing the socket, a nut or bolt head of the same size as that the wrench is intended to fit should be placed in the hole and the socket finished over this, between swages. A better way of

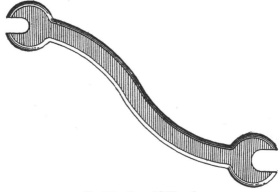

Fig. 114. Forged S-Wrench

making wrenches of this kind is to make a forging having the same dimensions as the finished wrench with the socket end left solid. The socket end is then drilled to a depth slightly greater than the socket is wanted. The diameter of the drilled hole should be, as shown in Fig. 117, equal to the shortest diameter of the finished hole. After drilling, the socket end is heated, and a punch of the same

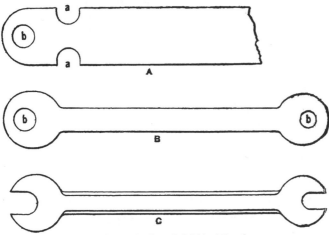

Fig. 115. Steps in Making Wrench

shape as the finished hole is driven into it. The end of the punch should be square across and the corners sharp. As the punch is driven in, it will shave off some of the metal around the corners of

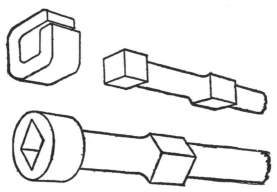

Fig. 116. Socket Wrench

the hole and force it to the bottom, thus making it necessary to have the drilled hole slightly deeper than the finished socket.

Ladle Shank. The ladle shank shown in Fig. 118 may be made in several ways. The ring may be welded up of flat stock and a round handle welded on with a T-weld, or square stock may be taken, worked out, and split as shown in Fig. 119, these split ends being afterward welded to make the ring. Another method of making without any welds at all would be to split the stock as indicated in

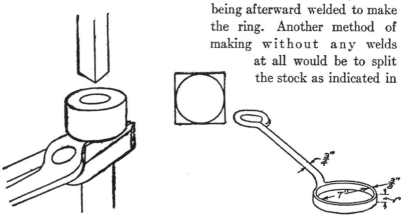

Fig. 117.   Making Hole in Socket Wrench   Fig. 118.   Ladle Shank

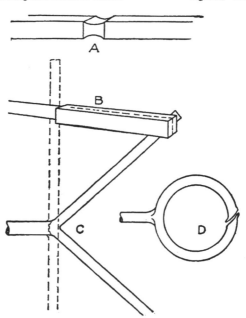

Fig. 119.   Ladle Shank Made from Square Stock

Fig. 120 and to work out in the same way that a weldless ring is made.   The latter method would take more time but would make the sounder forging.

Molder's Trowel. The molder's trowel illustrated in Fig. 121 is a sample of a large class of forgings, having a wide thin face with a comparatively small thin stem forged at one end. The stock used for the trowel would be about ¼ inch by 1 inch. This is thick enough to allow for the formation of a ridge at R. Fig. 122 shows the general method employed. Two nicks are first

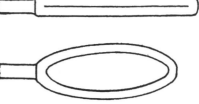

Fig. 120. Ladle Shank without Weld

made with fullers, as illustrated at A, and the stem drawn down, roughly, to size. This stem is then bent up at right angles and forged to a square corner, as illustrated at B, in the same general manner as the square corner of a bracket is formed. When flattening out the blade in order to leave the ridge shown at R, Fig. 121, the work should be

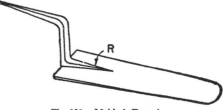

Fig. 121. Molder's Trowel

held as shown at C, Fig. 122. Here the handle is held pointing downward and against the side of the anvil. By striking down on the work and covering the part directly over the edge of the anvil with the blows, all the metal on the anvil will be flattened down. By swinging the piece around into a reversed position, the other edge of the blade is then thinned down. This

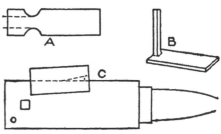

Fig. 122. Method of Making Molder's Trowel

leaves the small triangle shown by the dotted lines unworked and forms the ridge shown at R. The same result could be obtained by placing the work flat on the anvil face and using a set hammer.

BEMENT STEAM DROP HAMMER
Courtesy of Niles-Bement-Pond Company, New York

FORGING

PART II

FORGING OPERATIONS—(Continued)

TOOL=STEEL WORK

Tool Steel. Although not strictly true technically, for ordinary purposes tool steel may be considered simply a combination of iron and carbon. The more common grade contains perhaps 1 per cent of carbon. Machine steel and wrought iron do not contain this element carbon to any great extent. If a piece of wrought iron or machine steel is heated red hot and then suddenly cooled, the metal remains practically as it was before heating, but if a piece of tool steel be subjected to this treatment, it becomes very hard and brittle. By a modification of this heating and cooling, almost any degree of hardness may be imparted to the steel.

Proper Forging Heat. Before attempting any work with tool steel, a piece of scrap steel is to be experimented with, heated and hardened several times at various heats until the manipulator is sure of the effect of the various heats upon the grain of the steel. The steel should also be experimented with to determine just how high a heat it will stand. When heavy forging is to be done, i.e., when the first rough shaping is done upon a tool, a comparatively high heat should be used. The steel should be forged at about what might be called a good yellow heat. The lighter hammering, when finishing, should be done at a lower heat, about the hardening heat, though very little, if any, hammering should be done below that point. If the grain of the steel has been raised by too high a heat, it can generally be quite decidedly reduced by a little hammering at some heat above the hardening temperature.

Standard Forms

Cold Chisels. The stock should be heated to a good yellow heat and forged into shape and finished as smoothly as possible. When properly forged, the end or cutting edge projects as shown at C in

Fig. 123. It is a good plan to simply nick this end across at the point where the finished edge is to come, and then, after the chisel has been tempered, this nicked end may be broken off and the grain examined. Whenever possible, it is a good plan to leave on a tool

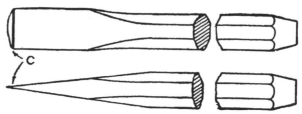

Fig. 123. Typical Views of Cold Chisel

an end of this sort that may be broken off after the tempering is done. When hardening, a chisel should be heated red hot about as far back from the cutting edge as the point *A*, Fig. 124. Care must be taken to heat slowly enough to keep the part being heated at a

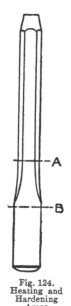

Fig. 124. Heating and Hardening Areas

uniform temperature throughout. If the point becomes overheated, it should not be dipped in water to cool off, but should be allowed to cool in the air to below the hardening heat and then reheated more carefully. When properly heated, the end should be hardened by dipping in cold water to the point *B*. As soon as the end is cold, the chisel should be withdrawn from the water and the end polished bright by rubbing with a piece of emery paper. The part of the chisel from *A* to *B* will still be red hot and the heat from this part will gradually reheat the hardened point. As this cold part is reheated, the polished surface will change color showing at first yellow, then brown, and at last purple. As soon as the purple (almost a blue color) reaches the nick at the end, the chisel should be completely cooled. The waste end may now be snapped off and the grain examined. If the grain is too coarse, the tool should be rehardened at a lower temperature, while if the metal is too soft, and the end bends without breaking, it should be rehardened at a higher temperature.

Cape Chisel. This is a chisel used for cutting grooves, keyseats, etc. The end *A*, Fig. 125, should be wider than the rest of the

blade back to *B*. The chisel is started by thinning down *B* with two
fullers, or over the horn of the anvil as shown at *A*, Fig. 126. The

Fig. 125. Cape Chisel

Fig. 126. Method of Forging Cape Chisels

end is then drawn out and finished with a hammer or flatter in the
manner illustrated at *B*. A cape chisel is given the same temper as
a cold chisel.

*Square- and Round-
Nose Chisels.* These two
chisels, the ends of which
are shown in Fig. 127, are
forged and tempered in practically the same way as the
ordinary cape chisel, the
only difference being in the
shape of the ends. Round-nose cape chisels are sometimes used for
centering drills and are then known as *centering chisels*.

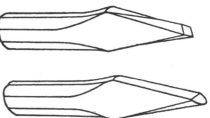

Fig. 127. Square-Nose and Round-Nose Chisels

Lathe Tools. The same general forms of lathe tools are used
in nearly all shops, but the shapes are altered somewhat to suit
individual tastes.

Right-Hand and Left-Hand Tools. Many lathe tools are made in pairs and are called right-hand and left-hand tools. If a tool is made in such a way that the cutting edge comes toward the left

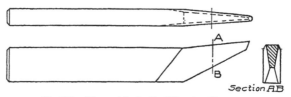

Fig. 128.   Views of Lathe Tool Showing Clearance

hand as the tool is held in position in the lathe, it is known as a right-hand tool, i.e., a tool which begins a cut at the right-hand end of the piece and moves from right to left. The one commencing at the left-hand end and cutting toward the right would be known as a left-hand tool. The general shape of the right-hand and left-hand tools for the same use is generally the same excepting that the cutting edges are on opposite sides.

Clearance. When making all lathe tools, care must be taken to see that they have proper clearance, i.e., the cutting edge must project beyond or outside of the other parts of the tool. In other words, the sides of the tool must be undercut or slant downward and backward away from the cutting edge. This is illustrated in the section *AB* of Fig. 128, where the lower edge of the tool is made considerably thinner than the upper edge, in order to give the proper clearance.

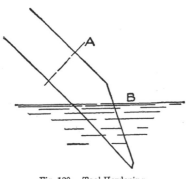

Fig. 129.   Tool Hardening

Round-Nose and Thread Tools. These tools are practically alike, excepting for a slight difference in the way the ends are ground. The general shape is shown in Fig. 128. When hardening, the tools should be heated about as far as the line *A*, Fig. 129, and cooled up to the line *B*. The temper is then drawn in the same general way as described for tempering of cold chisels, excepting that when a light yellow color shows at the cutting edge the tool is cooled for the second time. All lathe tools are given practically the same temper. Sometimes tools are left much harder. In one quite well known plant the tools are simply reheated until the water evaporates from the cutting end, indicating a reheating to a temperature of about 200° Fahrenheit.

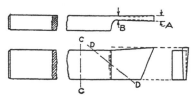

Cutting-Off Tool. Cutting-off tools are forged with the blade either on one side or in the center of the stock. The easier way to make them is to forge the blade

Fig. 130.   Typical Cutting-Off Tool

with one side flush with the side of the tool, as shown in Fig. 130. For use in a lathe the tool is generally forged on the left side so as to leave the cutting blade straight on the side toward the face plate of the lathe. For planer work, tools are often made in the center of the steel. The cutting edge, the extreme tip A, of the blade, should be wider than any other part of the thinned part B, in other words, this edge should have clearance in all directions as indicated in the drawing. The clearance angle at the end of the tool, as shown in the sketch, is generally about 20 degrees.

For hardening, heat very little of the steel except the blade; the end of the tool should be heated about as far as CC, and cool to

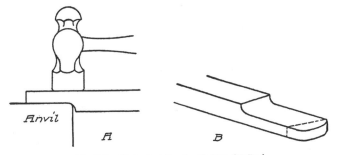

Fig. 131.   Method of Forging Cutting-Off Tool

about the line DD, enough so that the heat left in the steel will not work toward the point of the tool too quickly. This heat which is left in the steel is for tempering or drawing, and care should be taken so as not to leave the tool hard at the section B, as here not hardness, but toughness, is required. Temper generally to dark straw color or about 430° Fahrenheit.

The tool is started by placing enough of the steel on the anvil to draw out to the length wanted. Part of the face of the hammer is extended a little over the side of the anvil, as shown at *A*, Fig. 131. After roughly shaping, the end is trimmed off with a hot chisel along the dotted lines shown at *B*.

Boring Tool. The general shape of this tool is shown in Fig. 132. The length of the thin end depends upon the depth of the hole in

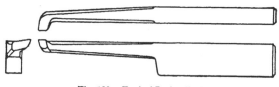

Fig. 132.   Typical Boring Tool

which the tool is to be used and as a general rule should be made as short and thick as possible, in order to avoid springing. The tool may be started in the same general way as the cutting-off tool, the fuller cut being made on the edge of the stock instead of on the side. The cutting edge of the tool is at the end of the small nose, and this nose is the only part which should be tempered.

Diamond Point. In Fig. 133 is shown the general shape of diamond points, and in Fig. 134 the different steps of making them.

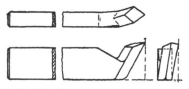

Fig. 133.   Typical Diamond Point Tool

The shape is started by using a bottom fuller, working the stock down about one-third, as shown at *A*. The rounded edge of the anvil can also be used in place of the fuller. Work down the point as shown at *B*, turning on the side as shown at *C* for starting the diamond shape, and working both sides until the proper size and shape are obtained. Then, placing the tool point on the flat side on the anvil, use a hot chisel to cut the point to the proper length, shown at *D*. In cooling this tool for hardening, leave but little heat in the rear end of the steel so as to draw slowly to light straw color, or about 410° Fahrenheit for even temperature, which means an even hardness in the point.

Side Tool. Side tools are generally started by drawing down a point endwise, as at *A* in Fig. 135. Hammer the point out at the corner of the anvil so that it can be drawn down small without striking the corner of the hammer into the anvil. Then bring the tool to the flat horn of the anvil for sharpening or drawing out thin on one side, as the top edge. Let part of the face of the hammer extend over the corner of the anvil so as to get the side hammered on the flat, with the recess all on the side that is down, as at *B*; then, placing

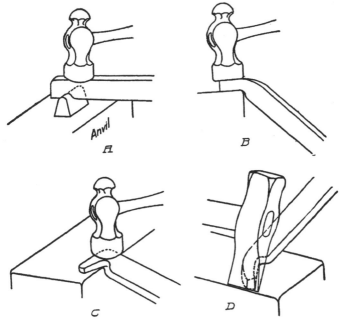

Fig. 134. Method of Forging Diamond Point

the tool on the anvil as at *C*, bend the top edge over to get the proper side clearance, as shown at *E*.

Hardening should be done by placing the tool blade in the cooling tank, as at *D*, and cooling off so as not to leave too much heat, causing the temper to come slowly. The tool is taken from the water, quickly rubbed bright on the flat side, and the temper drawn until the cutting edge shows a light yellow. The same color should show the entire length of the cutting edge. If the color shows darker at one end, it indicates that that end of the blade was not cooled enough, and the tool should be rehardened, this time dipping in such a way as to bring deeper in the water that end of the blade which was too soft before.

Centering Tool. The centering tool shown in Fig. 136 is used for starting holes on faceplate and chuck work. The end may be

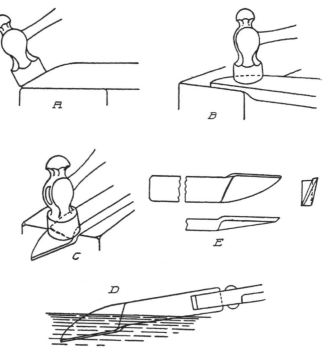

Fig. 135. Method of Forging and Hardening Side Tool

shaped by making a fuller cut and then flattening out the metal, trimming the cutting edge to shape with the hot chisel.

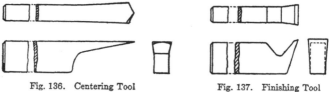

Fig. 136. Centering Tool   Fig. 137. Finishing Tool

Forming Tools. Forming tools for turret lathes are sometimes forged up in the same general shape as above and tempered like other lathe tools.

Finishing Tool. This tool, Fig. 137, may be started either with a fuller cut or in the same way as the diamond point. The end is then flattened out and shaped with a set hammer as shown in Fig. 138. This generally leaves the end bent out too nearly straight, but it may be easily bent back into shape as indicated at *B*. This bending will probably leave the point something like *C*. A few blows of the hammer at the point indicated by the arrow will give the tool the shape as at *D*. The cutting edge should be tempered the same as for other lathe tools. For planer and shaper tools of this shape, the end should be more nearly at right angles to the edge of the tool, making an angle of about 6 or 8 degrees less than the perpendicular; in other words, the tool should have less end rake.

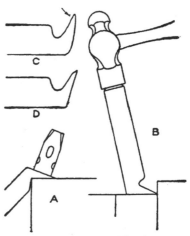

Fig. 138. Method of Shaping Finishing Tool

Flat Drill. Flat drills need no particular description as to forging and shaping. The size of the drill is determined by the width of the flat end, this being the same size as the hole the drill is intended to bore. If this dimension were 1 inch, the drill would be known as 1-inch drill. The drill should be made somewhat softer than lathe tools, the temper being drawn until a light brown shows at the cutting edge.

Springs. Springs are generally tempered in oil. The spring is heated to a uniform hardening heat and hardened by cooling in oil, usually lard or fish oil, as mineral oil is too uncertain in composition. The temper is drawn by holding the spring, still covered with oil, over the flame of the forge, and by heating until the oil burns over the entire spring. If the spring is not uniform in section throughout, it is generally advisable, while heating, to plunge it every few seconds into the oil bath, taking it out instantly and continuing the heating. This momentary plunge tends to equalize the heat by cooling the thinner parts.

The above method of tempering is known as blazing off, the

blazing point of the oil being used to indicate the temperature in place of the color of the scale. The same results could be obtained

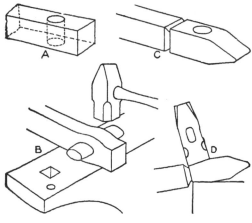

by polishing the spring and heating until it turned blue.

Hammers. When making a hammer the stock should be taken large enough to make the largest part of the hammer without any upsetting. As a general rule the hammer is forged on the end of a bar and is finished as completely as possible before cutting off.

Fig. 139. Method of Making Hammer

Riveting Hammer. About the easiest hammer to shape is the riveting hammer shown at *D*, Fig. 8. This hammer, as well as all other hammers, is started by first punching the hole for the eye as shown at *A*, Fig. 139. When the eye is punched the stock is generally bulged out sideways, and, in order to hold the shape of the eye while flattening down this bulge, a drift pin such as shown in Fig. 140 is used. This pin is made larger in the center and tapering at both ends. The center or larger part of the pin has the same shape as the finished eye of the hammer. This pin is driven into the punched hole and the sides of the eye forged into shape, as illustrated at *B*, Fig. 139. After the eye has been properly

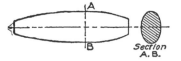

Fig. 140. Drift Pin

Fig. 141. Hardening Hammer Head

shaped, the next step is to shape down the tapering peen leaving the work, after a nick has been made around the bar where the face of the hammer will come, as shown at *C*. The end of the hammer toward the

face is then slightly tapered in the manner indicated at D. After the
hammer has been as nearly as possible finished, it is cut from the bar
and the face trued up. For tempering, the whole hammer is heated to
an even hardening heat. The hammer is then grasped by placing one
jaw of the tongs through the eye. Both ends are tempered, this
being done by hardening first one end and then the other. The
small end is first hardened by dipping in the water as shown at
Fig. 141. As soon as this end is cooled the position of the hammer is
instantly reversed and the face end hardened. While the large end
is in the water the smaller end is polished and the temper color
watched for. When a dark brown scale appears on the small end

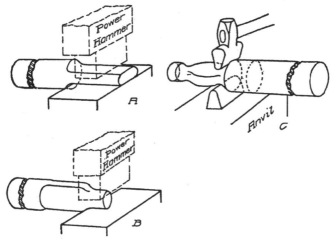

Fig. 142. Method of Making Ball-Peen Hammer

the hammer is again reversed bringing the large end uppermost and
the peen in the water. The face end is then polished and the temper
drawn. If the large end is properly hardened before the temper
color appears on the small end, the hammer may be taken completely out of the water, the large end polished, and the colors
watched for on both ends at once. As soon as one end shows the
proper color it is promptly dipped in water, the other end following
as soon as the color appears there; the eye should never be cooled
while still red hot. For some work hammer faces should be left harder,
but for ordinary use the temper as given above, is very satisfactory.

Ball-Peen Hammer. The general method of making a hammer
of this kind is illustrated in Fig. 142. Starting with round stock

(carbon steel), flatten under a power hammer, if one is available, as at *A;* otherwise use a set hammer on an anvil in the same manner, and then work enough down for the ball peen, as shown at *B.* Then fullers are used as at *C,* to space off for the hole to be punched between the octagonal parts formed with the fullers. To keep from flattening the part through which the hole is punched, it should be placed on a bottom fuller of the proper size. Care should be taken not to heat the steel too hot for this operation, as heat cracks are sure to take place. The steel should be of fairly high carbon; not less than 1 per cent. Harden and temper to about dark straw color, or 430° Fahrenheit.

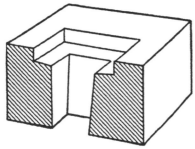

Fig. 143.   Block for Upsetting

Blacksmith's Tools. Such tools—cold chisels, hot chisels, set hammers, and flatters—are made in much the same way as hammers. The wide face of the flatters may be upset by using a block such as is shown in Fig. 143. The heated end of the tool is dropped into the hole in the block and the face upset into the wide shallow opening. Swages may also be worked up in this way.

MISCELLANEOUS PROCESSES

Shrinking. When iron is heated it expands, and upon being cooled it contracts to about its original size. This property is utilized

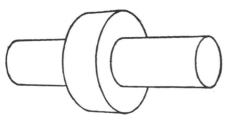

Fig. 144.   Collar Shrunk on Shaft

in doing what is known as shrinking. Fig. 144 shows a collar shrunk on a shaft. The collar and shaft are made separate, the hole through the collar being slightly less in diameter than the outside diameter of the shaft. The collar is then heated red hot and the heat causes the collar to expand, making the hole larger in diameter than the shaft. The collar, while still hot, is then placed on the shaft in proper position, and cooled as quickly as possible by pouring water on it. As

TABLE IV*

Color Scale of Iron Heats

COLOR	TEMPERATURE (Degree Fahrenheit)
Red, lowest visible in dark	878
Red, lowest visible in daylight	887
Red, dull	1100
Red, full	1370
Red, light (scaling heat)	1550
Orange, full	1650
Orange, light	1725
Yellow, full	1825
Yellow, light	1950

the collar is cooled it contracts and squeezes, or locks, itself firmly in position. This principle of shrinking is used to a large extent where a firm, tight fit is wanted, the only objection being that it is rather difficult to take a piece off after it has once been shrunk into place.

Allowance for Shrinkage. In doing work in the blacksmith shop it must be constantly remembered that the work is larger when being worked than it is when cool. Allowance must, therefore, always be made for shrinkage. As the pattern-maker allows for the contraction of the molten metal to the cold casting, so the blacksmith must allow for the contraction of the hot iron or steel to the cold forging.

From the scale of iron heats at the several colors, given in Table IV, it will be seen that the temperature at which forgings are finished under the hammer, should be at about 900° Fahrenheit. When these same forgings are cold their temperature will be from 60° to 70° Fahrenheit. There is, therefore, a difference of at least 840° between the working and the finished temperature. The expansion of iron may be taken to average about .00000662 of its length for each increase of one degree Fahrenheit in its temperature. If a bar of machine steel exactly 2 feet long when cold is heated red hot and measured, it will be found to have increased nearly $\frac{1}{4}$ inch in length. Taking the temperature of the red heat as 1370° Fahrenheit, and that of the cold bar as 70° Fahrenheit, the increase in length would be $1300 \times .00000662 \times 24$ (length in inches) $= 0.206$ inches. This expansion must be allowed for when measuring forgings red hot.

*Table IV is based on temperatures given by Messrs. Taylor and White, Transactions American Society of Mechanical Engineers, Vol. XXI.

Brazing. When two pieces of iron or steel are welded together, they are joined by making the pieces so hot that the particles of one piece will stick to those of the other, no medium being used to join them. In brazing, however, the brass acts in joining two pieces of metal together in somewhat the same manner that glue does in joining two pieces of wood. Briefly the process is as follows: The surfaces to be joined are cleaned, held together by a suitable clamp, heated to the temperature of melting brass, flux added, and the brass melted into the joint. The brass used is generally in the shape of *spelter*, which is a finely granulated brass which melts at a comparatively low temperature. Spelter comes in several grades designated by hard, soft, etc., the harder spelters melting at higher heat but making a stronger joint. Brass wire or strips of rolled brass are sometimes used in place of spelter, brass wire in particular being very convenient

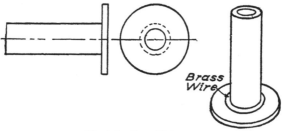

Brass Wire

Fig. 145.   Brazed Joints

in many places. A simple example of a brazed joint is shown in Fig. 145, where a flange is brazed to the end of a small pipe. It is not necessary in this case to use any clamps as the pieces will hold themselves together. The joint between the two should be made roughly. If a tight joint be used there will be no chance for the brass to run in. The joint should fit in spots but not all around. Before putting the two pieces together, the surfaces to be joined should be cleaned free from loose dirt and scale. When ready for brazing the joint is smeared with a *flux* (1 part sal ammoniac, 6 or 8 parts borax) which may be added dry or put on in the form of a paste mixed with water. The joint is then heated and the spelter mixed with flux sprinkled on and melted into place. Brass wire could be used in place of the spelter in the manner indicated, the wire being bent into a ring and laid round the joint as shown. Ordinary borax may be used as a flux, although not as good as the mixture used above. The heat

should be gradually raised until the brass melts and runs all around
and into the joint, when the piece should be lifted from the fire and
thoroughly cleaned by scraping off the melted borax and scale. It is
necessary to remove the borax, as it leaves a hard glassy scale which
is particularly disagreeable if any filing or finishing has to be done to
the joint. This scale may be loosened by plunging the work while
still red hot into cold water. Almost any metal that will stand the
heat, may be brazed. Great care must be used in brazing cast iron
to have the surfaces in contact properly cleaned to start with, and
then properly protected from the oxidizing influences of the air and
fire while being heated.

Bending Cast Iron. It is sometimes necessary to straighten a
casting which has become warped or twisted. Cast iron may be
twisted or bent to quite an extent if worked cautiously. The bend-

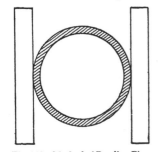

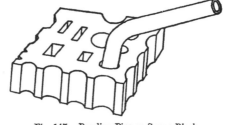

Fig. 146. Method of Bending Pipe   Fig. 147.   Bending Pipe on Swage Block

ing may generally be done at about the ordinary hardening heat of
tool steel and should be done by a steadily applied pressure, not by
blows. There is more danger of breaking the work by working it at
too high a heat than by working at too low. As an example of how
iron may be twisted, a bar of gray cast iron 1 inch square and a foot
long may be twisted through about 90 degrees before it will break.

Pipe Bending. A piece of pipe when bent always has a tendency
to collapse, and, if this collapsing can be prevented by keeping the
sides of the pipe from spreading, a pipe may be successfully bent into
almost any shape. One way of doing this would be to bend the pipe
between two flat plates as shown in Fig. 146, the plates being the
same distance apart as the outside diameter of the pipe. In bending
large pipe, the sides are sometimes prevented from bulging by working in with a flatter. Where a single piece is to be bent, it may be

done by heating the pipe and inserting one end in one of the holes in a swage block as shown in Fig. 147, the pipe being then bent by bearing down on the free end. As soon as a slight bend is made it is generally necessary to lay the pipe flat on the anvil and work down the bulge with a flatter. Where many pieces are to be bent, a grooved jig such as shown in Fig. 148 is sometimes used. The jig is of such a shape that the pipe is completely surrounded where it is being bent, thus not having any opportunity to collapse or bulge. Pipe is sometimes filled full of sand for bending. This helps to some extent. Care must be taken to see that the pipe is full and that the ends are solidly plugged. For bending thin copper tubing, it may be filled with melted rosin. This gives very satisfactory results for this character of work. After

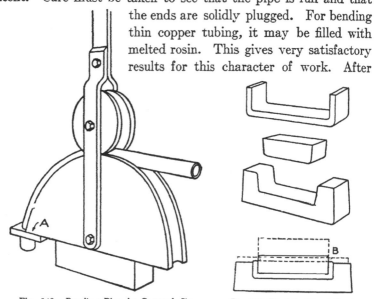

Fig. 148. Bending Pipe in Grooved Jig   Fig. 149. Block for Simple Bend

bending, the rosin is removed by simply heating the pipe.

Duplicate Work. Where several pieces are to be exactly alike in a shop that is not equipped for special work, it is sometimes practical to use a jig for performing the operations. For simple bending the jig may consist of a set of cast-iron blocks. Fig. 149 illustrates a simple bend with the block used for doing the work. The work is done as shown at *B*. The piece to be bent is placed, as shown by the dotted lines, with the bending block on top. The bending is done by one or two strokes of the steam hammer. For convenience in handling, the bending blocks are sometimes held by a spring handle as shown in Fig. 150. The blocks in this case are for bending the hooks shown at A. The handle is simply a piece of $\frac{1}{2}$ inch round iron with the ends screwed into the cast-iron blocks and held firmly by the lock nuts shown. This makes a cheap arrangement for

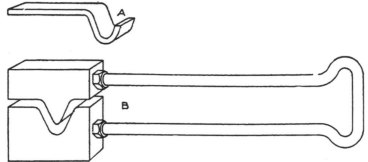

Fig. 150.   Spring-Handled Bending Jig

a variety of work, as the same handles may be used on various sets of blocks. Where a great number of pieces are to be made, these blocks or bending dies may be made of such a shape that they can be keyed on the steam hammer in place of the regular flat dies.

Die Forging. Pieces are sometimes shaped between formed steel dies where many are to be made exactly alike. An example of this sort of work is the eye bolt, Fig. 151. Round stock is used and is first shaped like A, Fig. 152. The shaping is done in the dies shown at B, which are simply two small blocks of tool steel fastened together with a spring handle, the inside faces of the blocks being formed to shape the piece as shown. The end of the bar is heated, placed between the die blocks and hammered until it takes the required shape, being turned through about 90 degrees between each two blows of the steam hammer, and the hammering continued until the die faces just touch. For the second step the ball is flattened to about the thickness of the finished eye and the hole punched under

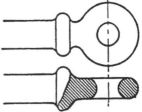

Fig. 151.   Eye Bolt

the steam hammer with an ordinary punch, leaving the work as shown at C. The final shaping is done with the finishing die D. This die is so shaped that when the two parts are together, the hole left is exactly the shape of the finished forging. In the first die it will be noticed that the holes do not conform exactly to the desired shape of the forging, being, instead of semicircular, considerably rounded off at the edges. This is shown more clearly in Fig. 153

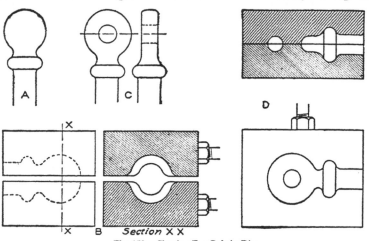

Fig. 152. Shaping Eye Bolt in Dies

at *A*, where the dotted lines show the shape of the forging, the solid lines the shape of the die. The object of the above is this: If the hole is semicircular in section, the stock, being larger than the smaller parts of the hole, after a blow will be left like *B*, the metal being

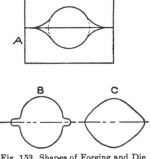

Fig. 153. Shapes of Forging and Die

forced out between the flat faces of the die and forming fins. When the bar is turned these fins are worked back and make a *cold-shut*. When the hole is a modified semicircle the stock will be formed like *C*, and may be turned and worked without danger of cold-shuts. Dies for this kind of work are sometimes made of cast iron. When made of tool steel it is sometimes possible to shape them hot. A master forging is first made of tool steel to exactly the shape of the required forging. The blocks for the dies are then forged with flat faces. These blocks are fastened to the handle and then heated red hot. The master forging is then placed between them and the dies hammered down over the forging, leaving the cavity just the proper shape.

HEAVY FORGING

Steam Hammer. An ordinary form of steam hammer is shown in Fig. 154. Its essential parts are an inverted steam cylinder, to whose piston rod the hammer head is attached, and the frame for carrying the whole. The hammer is raised by admitting steam beneath the piston. The blow is dealt by exhausting the steam from beneath the piston and admitting above. The head is thus accelerated by gravity and by the pressure of steam above the piston. The valve gear is so arranged that the intensity of the blow may be varied by changing the amount of steam admitted to the piston on its downward stroke. The steam admitted below on the same stroke forms a cushion for the absorption of the momentum of the head. In this way the lightest of taps and the heaviest of blows can be delivered by the same hammer. These hammers are also made in a great variety of sizes. Steam hammers are rated by the weight of the falling parts, i.e., the piston rod, ram or head, and hammer die. A hammer in which these parts weigh 400 pounds

Fig. 154. Typical Steam Hammer
Courtesy of Niles-Bement-Pond Company.

would be called a 400-pound hammer. Steam hammers are made in two distinct parts: the frame, carrying the hammer or ram, and the anvil, on which the hammer strikes. The frame is carried on a heavy foundation, and the heavy anvil, which is generally made of cast iron and fitted with a die block of tool steel, rests upon a heavier foundation of timber or masonry capped with a timber. The object of these separate foundations is to allow the anvil to give slightly under a blow without disturbing the frame. On very light power hammers the anvil and frame are sometimes made together.

Hammer Dies. The dies, as most commonly used with a steam hammer, have flat faces. The best ones are made of tool steel. These

dies may be made of tool steel and left unhardened, then when the
dies become battered out of shape from use, they may be trued up
and refaced without going to the trouble of annealing and hardening.
Dies of gray cast iron and cast iron with a chilled face are also quite

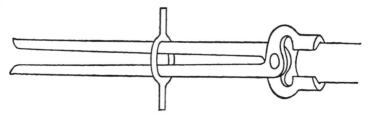

Fig. 155.   Tongs for Heavy Work

commonly used.   Ordinary gray cast iron is used, particularly when
special shaped dies are employed for welding and light bending.

Tongs.   Tongs for steam-hammer work should always be fitted
carefully, and should grip the stock firmly on at least three sides.
A quite common shape for tongs for heavy work is shown in Fig. 155.
To hold the tongs securely on the work and to make it easier to handle
them, a link is sometimes used of the shape shown.   This is driven
firmly over the handles of the tongs and the projecting ends are used
as handles for turning the work.

Hammer Chisels.   The common shape for hot chisels for use
under the steam hammer is given in Fig. 156.   The handle and blade

Fig. 156.   Steam Hammer Chisels   Fig. 157.   Sections of Chisel Blades

are sometimes made from one piece of tool steel.   Sometimes the
blade is made of tool steel and an iron handle welded on as shown in
the sketch.   The handle next to the blade should be flattened out
to form sort of a spring which permits a little give when using the
chisel.   The edge of the chisel should be left square across and not
rounding.   The proper shape is shown at *A*, Fig. 157.   Sometimes

for special work the edge may be slightly beveled as at *B* or *C*. For cutting or nicking bars cold, a chisel similar in shape to Fig. 158 is sometimes used. This is made very flat and stumpy to resist the crushing effect of heavy blows. For cutting into corners a chisel

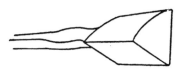

Fig. 158. Chisel for Cutting Cold Bars

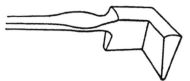

Fig. 159. Chisel for Cutting Into Corners

similar in shape to Fig. 159 is sometimes used. For bent or irregular work the chisel may be formed accordingly. For cutting off hot stock the method used is about as illustrated in Fig. 160, i.e., the work is cut nearly through as shown at *A*. The bar is then turned over and a thin strip of steel with square corners placed on top as

shown at *B*. A quick heavy blow of the hammer drives this steel bar through the work and carries away the thin

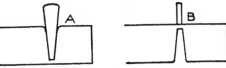

Fig. 160. Method of Cutting Off Hot Stock

fin shown, leaving both of the cut ends clean and smooth.

Tools. *Swages.* The tools used for steam-hammer work are generally very simple. Swages for finishing work up to 3 or 4 inches in diameter are commonly made in the shape shown in Fig. 161. The handle is made in the shape of a spring and may be either made in one piece with the blocks and drawn out as shown at *C*, or may be inserted as shown at *B*. This sort of tool is known as a *spring tool.* Another sort of swage sometimes

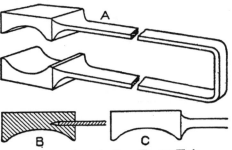

Fig. 161. Swage for Steam-Hammer Work

used is illustrated in Fig. 162, the top swage at *A*, the bottom swage at *B*. This sort of swage is used on a die block which has a square hole cut in its face similar to the hardie hole in an anvil. The short horn X, of the swage, fits into this hole, the other two projections coming over the side of the anvil block.

Tapering and Fullering Tool. The faces of the anvil and hammer dies are flat and parallel, and it is, of course, impossible to finish tapering work smooth between the bare dies. This work may be done by using a tool similar to Fig. 163. Its method of use is shown in Fig. 164, the roughing being done with the round side down and the finishing with the flat side. Fullers used for ordinary hand

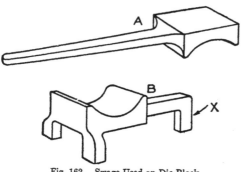

Fig. 162. Swage Used on Die Block

forgings are seldom employed in steam-hammer work. Round bars are used in their place in the manner illustrated in Fig. 165. If a nick is wanted on one side only, simply one round bar is used. Care must always be taken to be sure that the work is in the proper posi-

End View

Fig. 163. Tapering and Fullering Tool

tion before striking a heavy blow with the hammer. To do this the hammer should be brought down lightly on the work thus bringing the piece to a flat bearing for the first blow.

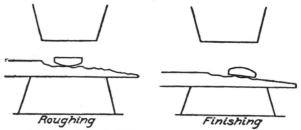

Roughing   Finishing

Fig. 164. Method of Using Tapering and Fullering Tool

Squaring up Work. It frequently happens that work is knocked lopsided under the hammer, being worked up into some such shape as shown at A, Fig. 166. To correct this and bring the work up

square, the bar should be put under the hammer and there knocked
into shape B, then rolled in the direction indicated by the arrow
until shaped as at C, when it may be worked down square and
finished like D.

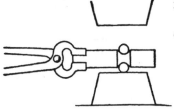

Examples of Work.   *Crank Shaft.*
The crank shaft shown in Figs. 91 and

Fig. 165.   Round Bars for Hand
Forging

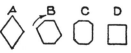

Fig. 166.   Squaring Up Work

92 is quite a common example of steam-hammer work.   The stock
is first worked as illustrated in Fig. 167, the cuts being on each
side of the crank cheek, and a special tool being used for this as
illustrated.   When the cuts are very deep, they should first be made
with a hot chisel and then opened up with this spreading tool.   With

light cuts, however, both operations may be done with a spreading tool at the same time.   Care
must be taken when flattening out
the ends, to prevent any of the
material from doubling over and
forming a cold-shut.   After the
ends are hammered out, the corners next to the cheeks may be
squared by using a block as shown
in Fig. 93.

Connecting Rod.   The forging
illustrated in Fig. 89, while hardly
the exact proportions of the connecting rod, is near enough the
proper shape to give a good example of this kind of forging.   The
work is first started by making

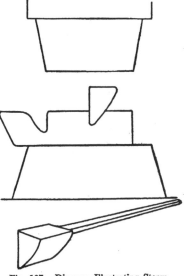

Fig. 167.   Diagram Illustrating Steam-
Hammer Work on Crank Shaft

two cuts as illustrated in Fig. 168.   The metal between the two
cuts is then drawn out by using two steel blocks, Fig. 169, until it
is stretched long enough for the corners of the blocks to clear the
hammer dies; then the work is done directly upon the bare die.

DROP FORGING

Development. Drop forgings were made first about 60 years ago, and from the necessarily crude methods which were first employed, the art of forging has developed into one of the largest branches of the mechanical arts. Great advancement has been made within the last few years, so that its scope of usefulness, as well as possibilities, are practically unlimited. This progress has been made possible by scientific investigations, improved machinery

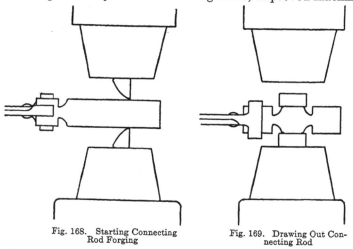

Fig. 168.　Starting Connecting
Rod Forging

Fig. 169.　Drawing Out Connecting Rod

and die materials, and especially by the exhaustive study of steel and its treatment.

The early history of drop forging shows that more or less depended on the skill of the blacksmith. He was obliged to work out the material by hand almost to the desired shape, then, with the aid of portable tools which were used in conjunction with the power and the steam hammer, the forgings were finished to uniform size. Corresponding to the development of machinery along other lines, however, it was only natural that the same progress should affect the forging business.

The sewing-machine, shoe-machine, harvester-machine, and automobile industries have been more instrumental than any other agencies in bringing stamp or drop forging to its present simplicity. From the fact that drop forging is purely mechanical, the word simplicity clearly signifies the methods used, which effect a wonderful reduction in the cost of production.

Forgings can be made in greater variety, and those that are most difficult or even impossible to finish over the anvil are made with apparent ease under the drop hammer. There seems to be no

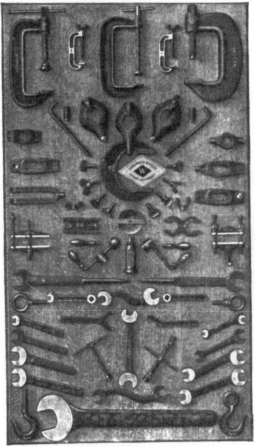

Fig. 170. Typical Drop Forge Tools
Courtesy of J. H. Williams and Company, Brooklyn, New York

limit to design, and the best feature of all is that the work is done more accurately, imparting a finish to every detail.

From the fact that to a great extent drop forgings have replaced malleable-iron castings, there is no doubt that new fields have opened to create a demand for forgings greater than would have developed if the mechanical world had been obliged to depend on the former methods of hand forging.

Process. Drop forgings are made by the use of dies. These dies are made in two parts and into them are sunk exact impressions of the parts wanted. One-half of the die is securely attached to the base of the hammer, the upper part being fastened to the ram which travels vertically between two guides. By continually raising and dropping this ram, the heated metal which is held between the two parts of the die is forced into the impressions cut into the dies. In forcing the metal into the die, there is a small amount called the *flash*, which overflows the impression. This flash is removed by a heavy turning press to which are attached dies cut to the correct size and shape to finish the forging.

In the process of forging, a thin scale is formed on the forging proper. This scale has to be removed in order that the finished

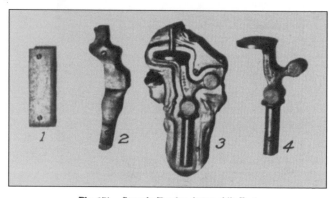

Fig. 171.   Steps in Forging Automobile Part

forging may be clean and smooth, and this is accomplished by a pickling process or by sand blasting. The pickling process consists of dipping each forging in a strong solution of acid which eats off all the scale.

Drop Hammer. To meet the requirements of an up-to-date forge shop, either of the types shown in Figs. 19 or 133 are suitable. They are almost indestructible machines, the capacity of which seems to be limited only by the ingenuity of the die sinker. The bases are of cast iron and in one piece, a weight ration of 15:1 between base and hammer being adopted. If the hammer weighs 2,000 pounds the base would weigh 30,000 pounds.

Specimens of Drop Forging. The light work illustrated in Fig. 170 is a group of drop-forged tools made by J. H. Williams and

Company, Brooklyn, New York, and shows some of the possibilities of drop forging.

Referring to Fig. 171, *1* is a portion of steel bar from which 1½-inch lathe dogs are forged in a 1,000-pound drop hammer; *2* is the material after sizing in an edger and being cut out on the side, also showing the tang or sprue by which the operator holds the piece— 3 blows of the hammer are required at this stage; *3* is the forging after the material has been fur-ther spread or "broken down" in the blanking or the roughing impression of the die—6 blows of the hammer are required here; *4* is the dog fully forged and with tail bent in the same operation, showing the fin or flash thrown out between the dies while forg-ing—6 to 7 blows of the ham-mer are required.

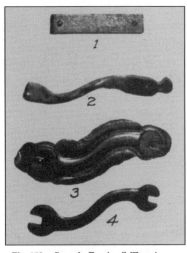

Fig. 172.   Steps in Forging S-Wrench

In Fig. 172 are shown the different steps for making an S-wrench in four operations, from stock 1⅛ inch wide and ½ inch thick, as at *1; 2* shows the rough-ing-die work; *3* shows the forging hammered down with flash not removed; *4* shows the forging finished and the flash trimmed off.

HEAT TREATMENT

Relation to Steel Development. The development of high-speed and of high-grade carbon steel has resulted in the development of scientific heat treatment. Where the process is applied, those cases in which operations are conducted in an accurate and intelli-gent manner apparently are in by far the smaller proportion. There seems to be less attention paid to heat treatment than to the com-position of the steel; but the heat treatment is far more important than a small variation in the chemical composition of the steel.

Proper Treatment Important. The physical changes which take place when a piece of steel is heated and quenched or slowly cooled are controlled by definite laws, and, with steels containing a high per cent of carbon with other alloying elements, the operation of heat-treating is a very delicate one, such that a slight variation even with the best of steel would give very poor results.

The proper or most practical heat treatments for the various steels have been determined by their manufacturers before placing them on the market, and the directions given should be carried out. To make one heat treatment which is satisfactory for all steels is impossible, so the manufacturers' recommendations should be followed.

Factors in Heat Treatment. Before going into the details of heat treatment, it is necessary to know some of the properties which enter into the steel, so as to understand the treatment more fully.

Steel, as we obtain it from the market at the present time, is a combination of iron and carbon and some impurities such as sulphur and phosphorus, though to produce particular results, these latter sometimes are added together with many other elements such as manganese, silicon, nickel, chromium, tungsten, molybdenum, vanadium, etc., either accidentally or purposely included for their effects.

Carbon Principal Determining Element. The principal element determining the properties of crucible tool steel is carbon. Pure iron is very nearly as soft as copper, while, with an increasing amount of carbon, steel becomes harder and stronger, but less ductile, until a carbon content of about 0.90 per cent is reached. Steel of this carbon content is the one mostly used for common machine-shop tools. Above this point other additions of carbon result in not only increasing hardness but also increasing brittleness.

Steels most generally useful in the hardened state have carbon from 0.90 per cent to 1.20 per cent, between which points the hardness is sufficient for almost every purpose. Steel containing carbon up to about 0.15 per cent carbon generally is called *ingot iron;* that from 0.15 per cent to 0.35 per cent is *machinery steel;* that from 0.35 per cent to 0.60 per cent is *crucible machinery steel;* and that from 0.60 per cent up is *tool steel.* Steels containing only carbon with small quantities of silicon, manganese, and the always present sulphur and phosphorus, generally are called *straight carbon steels.* Those owing their peculiar properties to some ingredients other than carbon are called *alloy steels.*

Critical Temperature in Hardening. For every grade of steel there is a so-called *critical temperature* or point of transformation. This temperature varies according to the various compositions and the carbon content of the steels. The phenomenon probably is more marked in the alloy steels than in straight carbon steels. On heating through the critical temperature or critical range the steel takes on hardness when cooled quickly, the hardness being according to its carbon content and the quickness of cooling.

When working a new steel for the first time, a blacksmith should acquaint himself with the particular hardening temperature of the material, and in practice he should be very sure not to vary or exceed it much.

Variation of Structure. To harden, steel must be heated to, or a little above, this critical temperature and be cooled suddenly, the percentage of hardness which the steel is capable of assuming being proportional to the speed of cooling—the quicker the cooling, the harder the steel. If heated below the critical temperature, even though quenched, steel does not take on hardness, but remains soft or partly annealed. On heating through the critical temperature, the previously existing structure is obliterated or tends to become obliterated, and up to this temperature, or just above it, is when steel possesses the finest structure which it is capable of assuming. The rate of obliteration of the old structure in a piece of steel depends upon the temperature reached and upon the time the steel is maintained at that temperature, the change proceeding more rapidly with increase of temperature. So, with the obliteration of the old structure, a new structure begins to grow, and its size increases with time and temperature, but more rapidly with increase of temperature than with increase of time at a lower temperature.

Once heated above the critical point and having reached the heat of hardening, steel may be cooled slowly to a certain degree and not lose its power of hardening if cooled suddenly. But to so let steel cool is very bad practice, because, during slow cooling, the micro-constituents of the steel tend to separate, as the coarser appearance shows on breaking the steel for the purpose of examining the grain. Below the critical temperature, slowness of cooling has no effect on the size of grain, but leaves the steel soft.

A bad practice sometimes followed by users of steel is to break off a bar of steel as it comes from the storehouse, examine the fracture, and if the steel shows a coarse grain, to condemn the steel. The appearance of the grain in the steel depends on its heat when it left the hammer or the rolling mill; if the heat were high, it would show a coarse grain; if the heat were low, it would show a closer fine grain. If the steel is heated to the proper hardening point afterward, the grain is the same, and there is no difference in its physical properties.

PROCESSES OF TREATING

Different Purposes. Steel is heated for four distinct purposes: (1) forging; (2) annealing; (3) hardening; and (4) tempering.

HEATING FOR FORGING

Uniform Heating Essential. In the first place, when steel is to be heated in a blacksmith forge, a clean deep fire is necessary for uniform results. If the fire is shallow, the steel oxidizes. The trouble in a forge fire usually is uneven heat, either too low or too high. Uneven heating causes strains from which trouble may result afterward in the form of fire cracks when tools are being hardened. It is essential that a piece of steel to be forged should be heated uniformly throughout its section, because if it is hot on the surface, and the interior is not yet up to heat, working it may break the center transversely, while if it is hot in the center and cold on the surface, generally the small surface cracks. Heat should be raised slowly and uniformly and should not be higher than is necessary for the work required. If through carelessness the heat rises too high, the temperature of the steel should be allowed to drop below the critical point and then should be raised to the proper point to avoid cracking the steel.

Trouble with Quick Heating. Suppose the piece to be forged has been put in a very hot fire and forced as quickly as possible to high yellow heat. If so treated, the outside will be soft and in good condition for forging, while the center parts will be not more than red hot. The highly heated soft outside will have very little tenacity, that is to say, this part will be so far advanced toward fusion that the particles will slide easily over one another, while the inside parts will be hard and possessed of high tenacity, and the particles will not slide so easily over one another.

Let the piece be placed under a hammer and forged, and the result is as shown in Fig. 173. The soft outside yields so much more readily than the hard inside that the outer part is full of small cracks, while the inside remains sound, and the piece is pronounced *burned.*

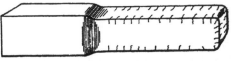

Fig. 173. Effect on Stock if Forged When Outside Is Too Hot

Exterior Too Cool. Suppose the case to be reversed, and the inside to be much hotter than the outside—that is, the inside to be heated to white heat, while the outside is hard and firm. Now, when the piece is forged, the conditions shown in Fig. 174 result. The outside is sound and the whole piece appears perfectly good until finished and cooled off and then

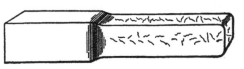

Fig. 174. Effect on Stock if Forged When Outside Is Too Cool

it is found to be a little hollow inside, and is branded *burst.*

In either case, if the piece had been heated soft all through, or if it had been heated only to red heat all through, it could have been forged perfectly sound.

Proper Forging Heat. Steel should be forged quickly with as few heats as possible, and should not be worked or finished when too cold. More steel is injured by hammering when too cold than when it is overheated; the usual excuse given for the former procedure being that it refines the grain—so it does, but it should be remembered that when steel has to be heated for subsequent hardening the effect of all the previous refining is obliterated.

If it is questioned then why there is ever any necessity for a smith to use a low heat in forging when high heat will do as well, it may be answered that in some cases a high heat may be more desirable to save labor, but that, in every case where a fine steel is to be used for cutting purposes, it must be borne in mind that too high a heat is apt to cause surface cracks; at the same time too low a heat and light hammer blows also will produce surface cracks.

Steel never should be allowed to soak too long in either a forge fire or a furnace after it has come up to a desired temperature, this having a tendency to decarbonize the steel and to make it coarse and brittle. Soaking does steel more injury than any bad practice known to the most experienced.

Simple Test of Heat Effect. A very simple method by which any worker in steel should be able to obtain a satisfactory test for the effect of heat upon steel is to take a bar of steel of ordinary size, say about 1 inch by $\frac{1}{2}$ inch, heat 6 or 8 inches of one end to a low red heat, and nick the heated part all around the bar at intervals of $\frac{1}{2}$ to $\frac{3}{4}$ of an inch, until eight or nine notches are cut. Next place the end of the bar in a very hot fire and heat it white hot until it nearly melts at the extreme end, leaving the other parts enough out of the fire so that they are heated by conduction. Let the end remain in the fire until the last piece nicked is not quite red hot, and the next to the last barely red hot. Now, if the pieces are numbered from 1 to 8, commencing at the outer end, No. 1 is white hot, No. 2 is yellowish white, No. 3 is high yellow, No. 4 is yellow or orange hot, No. 5 is high red hot, No. 6 is red hot, No. 7 is low red hot, and No. 8 is black. As soon as heated, let the bar be quenched in cold water and kept there until quite cold.

After cooling, the bar should be wiped dry carefully, especially on the notches. An examination by the file reveals the following, if high-carbon steel has been used: piece No. 1 scratches glass; Nos. 2, 3, and 4 are excessively hard; Nos. 5 and 6 are well hardened; No. 7 is about hard enough for tap steel; No. 8 is not hardened. Now break off the pieces over the corner of the anvil—they should be caught in a clean keg or box to keep the fracture clean and bright; No. 1 is found to be as brittle as glass with a coarse yellowish and very lustrous grain; No. 2 is found to be nearly as brittle and not quite so coarse or yellow; and so on, until Nos. 6 and 7 are reached— these are very strong with a finer grain; No. 8 is unhardened and shows the original grain of the bar.

ANNEALING

General Process. Steel is annealed for two distinct reasons: (1) to soften the metal for machining; and (2) to relieve the strains in the steel caused by hammering or by bending in the mill or the forge shop.

The process is heating, and then slow cooling. The steel should be heated a little above its critical temperature; for if heated below this temperature, all strain in the steel is not released and warping takes place when the hardening heat is reached.

As is noted under "Hardening", the rapidity of cooling determines the final hardness of the steel and if the steel is cooled very slowly it will be left very soft; while if cooled rapidly, it will be left hard. This difference in the cooling time is the only difference between its hardening and its annealing. Both should be done from the same heat.

Annealing High=Speed Steel. For good results in annealing high-speed steels, the following rules must be observed:

(1) Heat should be as near to 1500 degrees as possible. If the heat reached were only 1250 degrees, the steel would retain its original hardness. If heated to 1700 or 1800 degrees, the steel would be soft but would show brittleness with a coarse grain. If there were a further increase in heat, the steel would become hard and unannealed, and the fracture from this temperature would be dull and lifeless and would show a marked decarbonization.

(2) The steel should be packed in boxes or pipes, in powdered charcoal or lime, and sealed with fire clay, and in packing it should be seen that no part of the steel comes in contact with the box or pipes. If the parts come together, that does no harm.

(3) The heating should be started slowly and there should be given plenty of time for cooling. If a forge fire is used for annealing, leave the box in the fire and let it remain until cold, or if the forge fire has to be used for other purposes, the box can be put in some place out of the way and then covered with ashes, lime, or better still, charcoal. In all cases a slow cooling is necessary. If a furnace is used, heat slowly to full red or about 1500° Fahrenheit. Hold the heat long enough to be sure of penetration through the box and the steel to be annealed, and then shut off the heat and let the steel cool off with the furnace.

Water Method. Another method is water annealing. If only a few pieces are to be annealed for quick use, heat the steel to between 750° and 800° Fahrenheit, plunge it into water which has been heated to about 150° or 160° Fahrenheit, and allow it to remain until it becomes the same temperature as the bath. The heating should be slow and uniform for good results. To heat rapidly will cause internal strains and is apt to increase the risk of rupture when the steel is plunged into the water.

This last method is not to be recommended as it is not effective on all high-speed steels.

Annealing Copper and Brass. The treatment of these two metals consists in heating them to a red heat and then cooling suddenly in cold water. When copper or brass is hammered to any extent, it becomes hard and springy, and, if it has to be further worked, it must be annealed or softened, otherwise it is almost sure to split.

HARDENING

Purpose. Hardening generally is understood to mean the heating of a piece of steel to a certain temperature and plunging it into a bath of some kind for the purpose of cooling it. While this definition holds good for most steels, a few alloy steels now on the market reverse this method; steels known as air-hardened or self-hardening obtain their hardest and toughest state by a slow cooling process rather than by a sudden one.

Two reasons may be mentioned for the desirability of hardening steel: (1) to give the steel a cutting edge such as is required for all cutting tools; and (2) to alter the static strength and dynamic qualities of the metal so it will give the best results for the moving parts of machinery.

Essential Features. To harden steel, therefore, it is requisite that the heating produce a change in the structure, and that the quenching which follows the heating retain the whole or a part of the elements produced by this change. It is therefore necessary, as in annealing, that the temperature of the steel be raised to a point slightly above the point of transformation.

Point of Transformation. As the point of transformation varies with the different ingredients which are alloyed with steel, it is necessary to find out where this point is in the steel to be hardened. A steel may be heated to 1300° Fahrenheit, which is above the point of transformation in some steels, and no change in structure may occur; therefore no result in hardness is obtained. If this same piece is heated to 1450° Fahrenheit, which may be considered the point of transformation in this piece, the intermolecular transformation which consists of the passage of the carbon from the combined into the dissolved state takes place, and the steel assumes the hardest state possible, if properly cooled.

Influencing Factors. Thus the factors which have an influence on the results of hardening are: (1) the nature and composition of the metal; (2) the temperature of the metal when quenched; and (3) the nature, volume, and temperature of the quenching bath.

Carbon Content. The constitution of a given steel is not the same in the hardened as in the normal condition, owing to the carbon not being similarly disposed. In the annealed or normal steel it is in the free state, while in a hardened steel it is in a state of solution which we may call martensite, and this contains more or less carbon according to the original carbon content of the steel. The composition, and therefore the mechanical properties, depend principally upon the carbon content, the mechanical properties being changed slowly and gradually by the increase in carbon.

In regard to mechanical properties, the higher the temperature above the critical point, the lower the tensile strength, and the less the elongation, which means that the steel becomes more brittle with each increase in temperature. Coarsening of the grain, reduction of the tensile strength, and elongation lead to the conclusion that in practice 40° Fahrenheit above the highest point of transformation is the extreme limit to which steel should be raised to obtain the best results in hardening. The same figures hold also for annealing.

Results. The results obtained in hardening steel are: increase of tensile strength and of elastic limit, and reduction of elongation —the effect being greater in proportion to the carbon content; and due to quenching at the proper temperature, greater homogeneity, which aids resistance to shock.

Preparatory Heating. The most important feature to be taken into consideration is the method of heating, which should be such that the tool may be brought slowly and evenly to the hardening point without coming into contact with air or any form of gas which would oxidize the steel. Great care should be used, first, to protect the cutting edges and working parts from heating more rapidly than the bodies of the pieces; next, that the whole part to be hardened be heated through uniformly without any part being visibly hotter than another. A good oil or gas muffle furnace, provided care is taken to assure proper combustion, makes the best heating medium. For small tools, etc., a lead bath is very good.

Liquid Baths. The liquid baths commonly used for heating steel preparatory to hardening are molten lead, cyanide of potassium, barium chloride, a mixture of barium and potassium chlorides and other metallic salts.

Anyone using any of these different baths cannot be too careful in preventing an accident. If there is ever so little moisture of any kind on the tool to be immersed, it causes the molten liquid to fly in all directions. Before putting any tool into the bath, be sure that it is perfectly dry. The safe method is to pre-heat all tools before immersing them.

Lead at any heat above 1200° Fahrenheit gives off a slight vapor which is poisonous. Cyanide of potassium should be carefully used, as it is a virulent poison. The furnaces for heating these liquid baths should be equipped with hoods to carry away the fumes. It is a very good idea to put powdered charcoal on top of the molten liquid as charcoal acts as a purifier.

Hardening Bath. As it is necessary to maintain the steel in the state it was at the moment quenching began, the quenching bath is a very important part of the process of hardening. The better the bath, the more nearly perfection is attained.

Various baths are used for cooling steel when hardening, on account of the different rates at which they cool the heated metal. An oil bath is used when the steel is wanted tougher and not excessively hard, as the oil cools the steel more slowly than water. Brine or an acid bath is used when the steel is wanted very hard, as they absorb heat more rapidly than water. For excessively hard work mercury or quicksilver is sometimes used, as it absorbs the heat very rapidly.

In the hardening of steels, the influence of the bath depends upon its temperature, its mass, and its nature, or, to express this in another way, upon its specific heat, its conductivity, its volatility, and its viscosity. With other things equal, the lower the temperature of the bath, the quicker the metal cools and the more pronounced is the hardening effect. Thus water at 60 degrees makes steel harder than does water at 150 degrees, and, when the bath is in constant use, the first piece quenched will be harder than the twentieth, owing to the rise in the temperature of the bath. Therefore, if uniform results are to be obtained, the bath must either be of a very large volume or be kept cool by some mechanical means; in other words, the bath must be kept at a constant temperature.

A bath consisting of a liquid which volatilizes easily at the highest temperature it reaches, from plunging the metal into it, forms a space filled with vapor around the steel which retards the cooling action of the liquid. Motion of the bath throws off this vapor, as it brings the liquid in contact with the metal and tends to equalize the temperature. To agitate the piece to be hardened gives better results than trusting to the volatility of the bath, as it is more energetic in distributing the vapor.

Quenching Tanks. *Essentials.* The main point to be considered in a quenching bath as mentioned before, is to keep it at a uni-

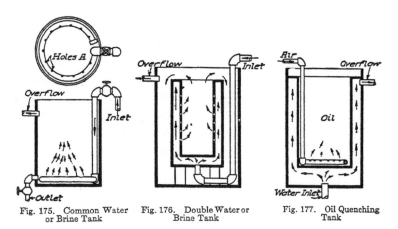

Fig. 175. Common Water or Brine Tank

Fig. 176. Double Water or Brine Tank

Fig. 177. Oil Quenching Tank

form temperature so that the successive pieces quenched will be subjected to the same heat. The next consideration is to keep the bath agitated, so that it will not be of different temperatures in different places. If thoroughly agitated and kept in motion as in connection with the tank shown in Fig. 176, it is not even necessary to keep the pieces in motion, as steam is not likely to form around the pieces quenched.

Common Tank. In Fig. 175 is shown a common water or brine tank. In this case, the water or brine is pumped from the storage tank and returned to it continuously. If the storage tank contains a large volume of water, there is no need of special means for cooling. The bath is agitated by the force with which the water is pumped into it. The holes at *A* are drilled on an angle so as to throw the water toward the center of the tank.

Double Tank. In Fig. 176 is shown the water or brine tank of a quenching bath. Water is forced by a pump or other means through the supply pipe into the intermediate space between the outer and inner tanks. From the intermediate space it is forced into the inner tank through small holes as indicated. The water returns to the supply tank by overflowing from the inner tank into the outer one and then through the overflow pipe as shown.

Oil Type. In Fig. 177 is shown an oil quenching tank in which water is circulated in an outer surrounding tank for keeping the oil bath cool. Air is forced into the oil bath to keep it agitated.

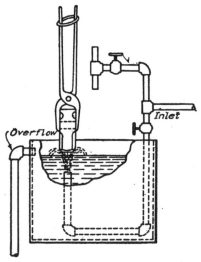

Fig. 178. Quenching Bath Used for Hammers, Etc.

Special Form. Fig. 178 shows a quenching bath used to harden the faces of hammers and all similar tools. The stream of water rising straight from the bottom of the quenching tank strikes the face of the hammer as shown and in this way insures the center being equally as hard as the edges, because steam cannot generate and form a cushion as it would were the tool merely immersed in the water.

Cracks and Fissures. Much serious trouble has been caused by the sudden cooling of the steel. Many times a piece separates abruptly from the part quenched. The reason for this is easily given, as, during the cooling, different parts of the steel are at different temperatures. This is many times caused by thick and thin sections in the same piece, but it also occurs in pieces of an even thickness, owing to the transformation in temperature not taking place everywhere at the same time. This causes internal strains which many times attain enormous value and result in the lessening and also stopping of the cohesive force which holds the molecules of the steel together.

Warping. Warping may be caused by several factors, of which the two most important are: not having the steel in a proper condition of repose before it is hardened; and not putting the piece in the quenching bath properly. As any operation of working the steel is liable to set up internal strains, it is always best after rolling, forging, or machining steel to thoroughly anneal the piece before hardening it. This allows the steel to assume its natural state of repose.

Preventive Rules. There are several rules that can be followed in hardening a piece of steel to prevent warping, and these rules always assume that the steel has been properly annealed before starting the hardening. (1) A piece never should be thrown into the bath, as by lying on the bottom it is liable to cool faster on one side than the other, thus causing it to warp or crack. (2) The piece should be agitated in the bath to destroy the coating of vapor which might prevent its cooling rapidly, and also to allow the bath to convey its heat to the atmosphere as required. (3) Work should be quenched in the direction of its principal axis of symmetry so that the liquid will cover the greatest possible surface at the instant of quenching. A gear wheel should be hardened perpendicularly to its plane, and a shaft vertically. (4) Hollow pieces such as spindles should have the ends plugged, as they could not be quenched vertically on account of the steam which would form in the hole. (5) Pieces with thin and thick sections or of intricate sections, should be immersed in such a manner that the parts of the greatest section enter first. (6) Pieces which are very complicated should be rigged up with hoops, clamps, or supports, to prevent their warping.

Carbonizing

Problem of Casehardening. During the last few years, when the universal aim of the designer and manufacturer has been directed to the highest efficiency of the product, a problem of a peculiar nature is sometimes met.

For a simple illustration, consider a pair of toothed wheels, or a chain and a sprocket, transmitting power. In either case, strength and durability are very essential in order to transmit the power safely and to retain the true surface of the tooth for the sake of good efficiency. It will be readily seen that, in order to meet such conditions satisfactorily, a material of a soft and tough nature should be employed—something that possesses strength and resistance to wear, and still conforms with standard practice of design regarding the proportions of parts. Such problems have come and have to be met by the manufacturer and the mechanic; they constitute the problem of *casehardening*. It is not a new subject but is one that is not well understood and not always easy to control. This statement is justified by the diversity of opinion among different investigators in regard to the fundamental principles underlying the process of casehardening.

Principles of Process. The process consists, as the name implies, of forming a case of high carbon, which is capable of hardening a surface of a low-carbon steel or wrought iron which in itself has not the property of hardness. The prevailing theory is based on the following principles.

(1) The steel to be carburized must be placed in contact with carbonaceous material.

(2) The high temperature at which the steel and the carbonaceous material is heated gasifies the carbon (if in a solid state) and opens the pores of the steel, allowing the gaseous carbon to penetrate.

(3) The penetration is aided if the gas is under pressure and in the presence of nitrogenous matter acting as a carrier of the carbon.

Carbonizing Materials. The most important factor involved in casehardening is the carbonizing material, for upon this depends quality of case and uniformity of product. The great difficulty at the present time is to obtain a definite uniform result, and to duplicate it at will. Many investigators are engaged in the solution of this problem which eventually will be solved by the discovery of a reliable carbonizing material.

Old Process. In the older process, charred organic matter—such as wood charcoal, charred leather, bone, horn, and the like—was used for packing. Charred leather being rich in nitrogen gave a very good result, but leather scrap became useful for other purposes, thus becoming unavailable for carbonizing. Granulated bone was next resorted to and is used extensively yet, but, owing to its high phosphorus content, it is apt to make parts brittle, and it should be avoided on small parts. Charcoal does not seem to find much favor, although it is fully as efficient as bone if properly prepared.

Opposing Factors. All of the materials mentioned are more or less unreliable for producing the desired effect on the steel. The question then arises, What would constitute a reliable material? Before replying directly, there must be considered the following factors which hinder the carburization of the steel by bone, charcoal, or similar prepared compounds.

(1) Unequal heating of the steel due to the manner of packing. It takes considerable time for heat to penetrate to the center containing the steel and packing; consequently, the parts near the walls of the crucible are heated sooner, and carbonizing begins earlier.

(2) Unequal composition of materials for packing causing variation in the amount of gas, and, therefore, unequal pressure generated in different sections of the crucible or packing box. To obviate this trouble, a packing material of perfectly uniform composition and high conductivity should be used. It should liberate carbon freely, yet not faster than the steel can absorb it. Steel absorbs carbon at certain rates depending on the temperature; high heat gives faster penetration. If an excess of carbon is liberated, the surface of the steel becomes supersaturated with carbon, the result being a brittle structure. The case should not be more than from 0.90 per cent to 1 per cent carbon, which is generally the result if proper heat and good carbonizing material are used. The packing material should be free from sulphur, especially if moisture is present, for sulphur acidifies moisture, and the combined effect produces a scaled pitted surface.

Compounds. There are a number of casehardening compounds on the market claiming one or more of the ideal characteristics. In general these compounds consist of: carbon, volatile matter and hydrocarbon, nitrogen, ash, sulphur, and phosphorus. They are likely to contain silica, alumina, lime, ammonia, and carbonate.

Use of Crucible. *Packing.* The parts to be casehardened should be placed in the crucible in such a way that none of them may come in contact with it, for otherwise the result would be soft spots; there should be a space of at least 1 inch from the wall of the crucible and about $\frac{1}{2}$ inch between the parts.

The packing material should be well tamped down so as to leave no open space. This is a very important and necessary precaution which must be observed to obtain a satisfactory result. After heating the contents of the crucible, a shrinkage takes place which amounts to about 16 per cent of the total value in the crucible. If the specimens are not packed tightly, some of them, or portions of them, are liable to be exposed and no appreciable carburization will result in the exposed surfaces. This statement simply reverts to the principles involved in carburizing with solid material, viz: There must be solid carbon in contact with the steel, and an intervening gas (CO) to effect carburization.

Sealing. Having carefully packed the specimens, the crucible should be covered with a lid and luted with fire clay. If neglected, this operation would cause an almost total failure—the specimen at the bottom would have a slight case; those on top would not have taken on any carbon. If the crucible is not sealed, the gases formed inside escape, which means, eventually, the absence of one of the principal elements in carburizing, viz, the intervening gas.

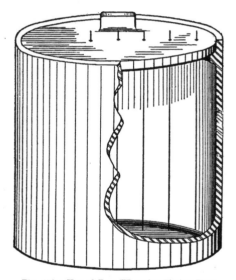

Fig. 179. Use of Test Wires for Timing Heat

Timing. To determine the length of time required for the crucible to heat through, the wire test is the safest. Steel wires $\frac{1}{16}$ inch in diameter are inserted through suitable holes in the cover into the packing mixture. Fig. 179 shows the manner in which they were placed. These wires are drawn one by one at different intervals and the temperature noted from the color of the wire. Suppose the outside wire is drawn and found to be up to heat. The next is drawn, and if not up to heat, as indicated by the color, more time should be given for heating. When the last wire is up to heat, count the time for carburizing.

Crucibles should not be too large. If so, the parts near the crucible wall take on more carbon due to being reached by the heat

TABLE V
Casehardening

Temperature (degrees F.)	Time (hours)	Case	
		Depth (inch)	Carbon (%)
1650	2	$\frac{1}{64}$	0.80
1650	4	$\frac{1}{32}$	1.00
1650	6	$\frac{1}{16}$	1.15

quicker. The average time required for packing the material and heating up the crucible should not be more than $1\frac{1}{2}$ or 2 hours.

Boxes for Packing. Ordinary cast-iron boxes are used mostly in the majority of shops and give good service if the heat used is not too high. Malleable-iron boxes stand a higher heat. If a heat of about 1800 degrees is required, a graphite crucible will give the best results.

General Packing. Observe the customary rules, allowing a sufficient amount of carbonizing material in proportion to the amount of steel to be carbonized. Pack uniformly for uniform results. Shake the box so that the carbonizing material will pack close to the steel. When the last layer of steel has been placed in the box, fill the latter heaping full with carbonizing material and tamp down with a wooden block. Cover the boxes and seal with fire clay.

Re=Using Carbonizing Material. Most of the compounds can be used over several times before being entirely exhausted, in from 50 to 75 hours, so by adding from 20 to 25 per cent of new material to the old each day there will be sufficient to provide for shrinkage and keep the carbonizer up to its normal strength.

Carbonizing Temperature. Most carbonizing material has a carbonizing range from about 1500° to 1800° Fahrenheit. The temperature should be chosen so that the core of the carbonized steel does not crystallize excessively. By observing this precaution, good results can be obtained with a single heat treatment. A temperature of from 1600° to 1700° Fahrenheit will suit the majority of carbon steels; the depth of case and percentage of carbon acquired in various times are shown in Table V.

Carbonizing and Hardening with One Heat. This is not a good practice, but is sufficient for some kinds of work. When this practice is resorted to, the heat must not be above 1600° Fahrenheit, or the steel will be coarse and brittle. A carbonizing heat of about 1500° Fahrenheit is better though it means a slower penetration.

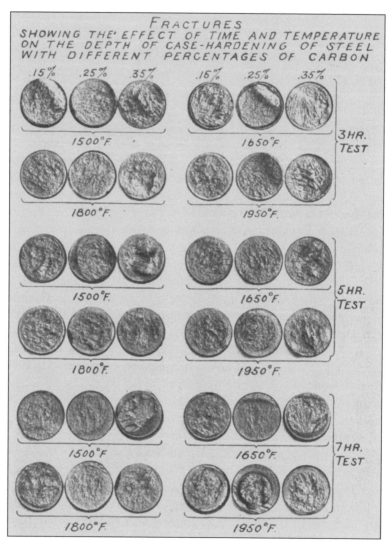

Fig. 180. Fractures of Steel Bars Showing Various Tests

Heat Treatment after Carbonizing

Shell and Core Distinction. The heat treatment following carbonizing should be done very carefully owing to the fact that the piece must have a very hard outer surface in order to resist wear and also a non-brittle core which will resist strains.

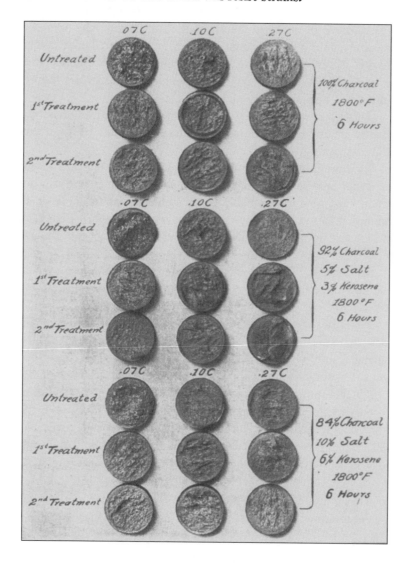

Fig. 181. Fractures of Steel Bars Showing Effect of Heat Treatment after Carbonizing

Double Quenching. For the best results, as the carbonizing temperature is a high one, the piece should be allowed to cool, then reheated to 1650° Fahrenheit and quenched, and reheated again to 1400° Fahrenheit and quenched.

The reason for the double quenching is that the piece must be heated above its point of transformation to destroy the crystallization and consequent brittleness which is liable to be in the core when it is carbonized at a high temperature; but this leaves the carbonated surface layer not hard enough to resist wear; therefore it must be quenched again at 1400° Fahrenheit.

This point of transformation varies with the different components of the high-grade alloy steels, and should be ascertained before hardening the piece.

By quenching directly from the carbonizing retort a distinct line is formed between the high-carbon outer shell and the low-carbon core, and this is liable to cause the metal to crack on this line, but if the work is properly heat-treated after carbonizing, this distinct line is made to disappear, and the danger of the steel cracking is removed.

Specimens. Fig. 180 shows the fractures of different samples of steel and the effect of time and temperature on the depth of case-hardening of steel with different percentages of carbon.

Fig. 181 shows the effect of heat-treatment after carbonizing. *Untreated* means that the steel was quenched direct from the carbonizing retort, which is too high a heat for good results. *First treatment* shows that steel was allowed to cool and then reheated to 1400° or 1450° Fahrenheit and quenched. This gives a good case but not a good core. *Second treatment* shows the results that come from proper heat-treatment. The steel was allowed to cool, reheated to 1650 degrees, quenched, reheated to 1450 degrees and quenched, which gives both a tough core and a hard fine-grain case.

Cyanide Hardening

Potassium=Cyanide Bath. Some hardeners prefer cyanide of potassium to lead for heating cutting tools, dies, etc. It is a white transparent salt which melts at a fairly low temperature, and should be carefully used as it is a virulent poison. The fumes are very injurious and the furnace should be enclosed with a hood connecting with a chimney or ventilating shaft. This bath is used a great deal in gun shops for hardening certain pieces on which it is wished to secure ornamental color effects. To get the color effect an air jet is forced up from the bottom of the quenching tank, as shown in Fig. 182, and the air coming in contact with the piece to be hardened gives it a variety of colors.

Casehardening. Casehardening also can be done with cyanide, although no great depth of case is secured. The cyanide is melted in a cast-iron pot in a furnace and then the work to be casehardened is entirely immersed in the cyanide which is heated to a dark cherry red. The work should be suspended by fine iron wires. When the work has been thoroughly heated through, it can be removed and quenched 15 or 20 minutes afterward, and a casing of suitable depth for ordinary purposes is insured. Increasing the length of time of immersion will simply add to the depth of the casing, but 30 minutes of heating will give a very deep casing. The work can be dipped in clear cold water immediately after having been removed from the cyanide bath,

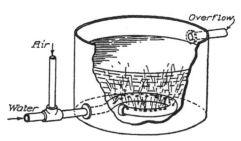

Fig. 182. Quenching Tank

or it may be permitted to cool, and may be reheated and hardened in the same manner as in connection with pack hardening. When small pieces are to be heated in cyanide, it is best to use wire baskets, which must be made so that the liquid has free access to all the surfaces of the finished pieces.

Tool Work

General Laws for Hardening. Because of the many grades of steel now made containing various alloys, it is impossible to give any set rules for hardening as compared with those used at the time when strictly straight carbon tool steel was used for all purposes. The hardening of a carbon steel is due to a change of internal structure which takes place in the steel when heated properly to a correct temperature. The two simple general facts of hardening that may be remembered are: (1) the heat from which the steel is cooled determines the grain; and (2) the rapidity of cooling determines the hardness, everything else being equal, the more rapid the cooling, the harder the steel.

Hardening Heat. There is only one heat from which the steel may be cooled and have the proper grain, and this is known as the *hardening heat*. A piece of steel when cooled from this hardening heat has an extremely fine silky looking grain and is left very hard and brittle. The hardening heat varies with the amount of carbon the steel contains, the greater the percentage of carbon, the lower the hardening heat.

To determine the hardening heat, a bar $\frac{1}{4}$ inch or $\frac{3}{8}$ inch square is heated to a good red heat on one end, and cooled in cold water. This end is then tested; if too hard to file it has been hardened, and the heat from which it was cooled was either the proper hardening heat or some higher heat. If the end can be filed, it was cooled from some heat below the hardening heat. If the end proves to be soft, it should be rehardened by cooling from a higher heat, if hard, it should be broken off and the fracture examined. If the grain of the broken end is very fine, the steel is properly hardened, if coarse, it was heated too hot and the end should be rehardened at a lower heat. The experiment should be repeated until the operator is able to give the steel a very fine grain every time. Any variation either above or below the hardening heat will make the grain coarse. A temperature lower than the critical heat will not make the steel as coarse in structure as a temperature correspondingly higher, but there will be some difference.

Self=Hardening Steel. Self-hardening steel is used to a large extent in modern practice for lathe tools, much being used in the

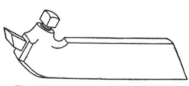

shape of small square steel held in special holders, as illustrated in Fig. 183. Self-hardening steel, as its name indicates, is almost self-hardening by nature, generally the only treatment that is required to harden the steel being

Fig. 183.　Typical Tool Using Blade of Self-Hardening Steel

to heat it red hot and allow it to cool. Sometimes the steel is cooled in an air blast or is dipped in oil. It is not necessary to draw the temper. The self-hardening quality of steel is given to it by the addition of chromium, molybdenum, tungsten, or one of that group of elements, in addition to the carbon which ordinary tool steel contains. High speed steel is lower in carbon.

Self-hardening steel is comparatively expensive, costing from 40 cents and upward per pound, some of the more expensive grades costing $1 or so. However, when in use, self-hardening steel will stand a much higher cutting speed than the ordinary so-called carbon steel, and for this reason it is much more economical to use, although its first cost is higher.

Self-hardening steel cannot be cut with a cold chisel and must be either cut hot or nicked with an emery wheel and snapped off. Great care must be used in forging it, as the range of temperature through which it may be forged is comparatively slight, running from a good red heat to a yellow heat. Some grades of self-hardening steel may be annealed by heating the steel to a high heat in the center of a good fire and allowing the fire and the steel to cool off together. Steel which has been annealed in this way may be hardened by heating to the hardening heat and cooling in oil.

Taylor-White Process. This method of treating special grades of self-hardening steel was discovered some years ago by the men after whom it is named. It was found that if a piece of self-hardening steel is heated to a very high temperature (about the welding heat) and then suddenly cooled to about a low red heat, the steel would be in a condition to stand very much harder usage and take a much heavier cut. Steel treated in this way seemed to have the cutting edge of the tools almost burned or melted off and considerable grinding was necessary to bring them into shape. When put in use the edges would almost immediately be slightly rounded or crumble off, but after this slight breaking down of the cutting edge, the steel would stand up under excessively trying conditions of high speed and heavy cut. Tools of this character are of very little or no use for fine finishing, but are of great value for heavy and roughing cuts.

Hardening High=Speed Steel. High-speed steel has a much higher critical temperature than carbon steels. A temperature of about 1350° to 1600° Fahrenheit is sufficient for carbon steels in general. High-speed steels require heating from 1800° to 2300° Fahrenheit, and to be cooled in oil such as machine, fish, or linseed. Steel of this nature is close grained and should be heated slowly until red, then forcing the heat faster up to dazzling white. When it shows signs of melting down it should be quickly put in the cooling bath. The treatment varies for the different steels, and it is advisable to get directions from the steel maker as to the treatment, which varies according to the alloys of the steel. Air blast formerly was recommended by some steel makers, but at present oil is most extensively used.

Barium-Chloride Bath. A barium-chloride bath for heating high-speed steel has been used by some manufacturers for finished tools such as milling cutters, taps, and drills. To get the high heat required without oxidizing, a thin coating of the barium chloride is formed on the steel, which, in transferring from the heating bath to the oil bath, keeps the steel from coming in contact with air and thus avoids oxidation. One trouble with the barium chloride is that a thin surface about 0.008 inch thick is soft, but for cutters that have to be ground this disadvantage is of no account.

Special Shapes. For tools with special shapes that cannot be ground—such as gear cutters, twist drills, taps, threading dies, and many other tools not permitting grinding after hardening—a muffle furnace is best to use, as in this furnace tools do not come in contact with the flame and the thin cutting points are thus more protected.

Measuring and Testing Instruments

Pyrometers. All up-to-date hardening rooms now are equipped with pyrometers in order to insure uniformity of the heat in the furnaces, and also uniform results in the hardened products.

There are various types of pyrometers, depending upon different principles for their workings such as the thermoelectric, resistance, radiation, and others. The most commonly used is the thermoelectric type. In this type, the temperature variations are determined by the measurement of an electric current generated by the action of heat on the junction of two dissimilar metals, that is, when one junction of the thermo-couple has a temperature different from the other, a current is developed which indicates on a meter.

Thermoelectric Type. Fig. 184 shows the outlines of the parts of a complete Wm. H. Bristol thermoelectric pyrometer, with the fire end applied for measuring the temperature in a bath of molten lead. This particular fire end is bent so that the tip *A*, where the elements are welded together and the temperature is measured, may be submerged in the molten metal and the fire end joined to the extension piece at the point C, so as to carry the cold end D of the thermo couple $ABCD$ to a point of constant temperature.

Method of Installing. Fig. 185 shows the method of installing a pyrometer in a muffle type of furnace with the fire end projecting through a hole in the rear wall. The fire end is provided with two iron-pipe protection tubes, so that when the outer pipe scales away through action of the heat, this can easily be replaced without injury to the elements of the fire end or its inside protection pipe. The diagram shows the extension piece installed horizontally so

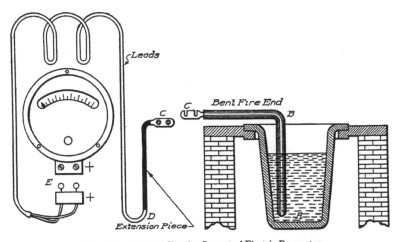

Fig. 184. Diagram Showing Layout of Electric Pyrometer

that it affords a practical method of keeping the cold end of the couple below and away from the influence of the variations of temperature in the furnace.

Accurate Use. As the temperature is measured at the tip of the fire end, the end should project far enough into the furnace to become thoroughly heated through. With the pyrometer to guide him, the operator can hold the right temperature in the furnace and make sure the work is heated up to this temperature by comparing its color with that of the tip of the fire end. For accurate results the cold end of the connection should be kept at a temperature of about 75° Fahrenheit.

It seems to be the general opinion among some people that pyrometers are not of much use in hardening, that they do not give accurate readings, and that better results can be attained by depending upon a man's experience. It is quite true that an experienced

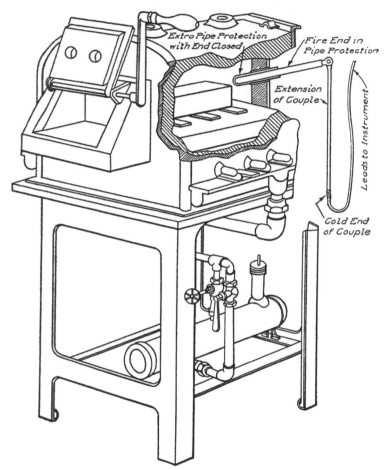

Fig. 185. Part Section Showing Method of Installing a Pyrometer in a Furnace

man's eye is a good means for judging the heat in a furnace and may be far better than an incorrectly calibrated pyrometer. However, by frequent calibration it is possible to keep the pyrometer in such condition that the readings are a great deal more accurate than any estimate of heat by the eye.

Hardness Testing. Few properties of iron and steel are of more importance than that of hardness, and even as far back as when men first began to harden steel, they probably sought some method of testing for hardness. Although the file test for hardness is used extensively today, it is not considered accurate. In regard to methods for testing hardness, it might be well to mention four, though of these four there are only two that are very well known

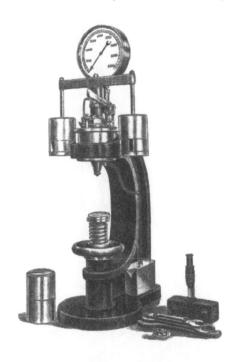

Fig. 186. Brinell Hardness Tester

and that are most commonly used—the Brinell test, brought out in 1900, and the Shore test, brought out in 1907.

Sclerometer. In 1886 Prof. Thomas Turner brought out the sclerometer. In this form of test a weighted diamond point is drawn across a smooth surface two or three times and the hardness number is the weight in grams required to produce a standard scratch.

Drill Test. Keeps testing is known as the drill test and was introduced in 1887. In this form of apparatus a standard steel drill is caused to make a definite number of revolutions when pressed with various standard forces against the piece to be tested. The hardness is automatically recorded on a diagram.

Fig. 187. Scleroscope Testing Set
Courtesy of Shore Instrument Company, New York City

Brinell Tester. Fig. 186 shows the Brinell method. In this method a hardened steel ball is pressed into a smooth surface of the metal so as to make an indentation which is measured by a microscope. The spherical area of the indentation being calibrated and the pressure being known, the stress per unit of area when the ball comes to rest is calculated, and then the hardness number is obtained.

The machine, Fig. 186, is an hydraulic press with a downwardly acting ram carrying the ball which is pressed into the test piece; the manometer shows the pressure of the oil.

Shore Scleroscope. Shore's scleroscope consists of a small cylinder of steel with a hardened point which is allowed to fall upon the

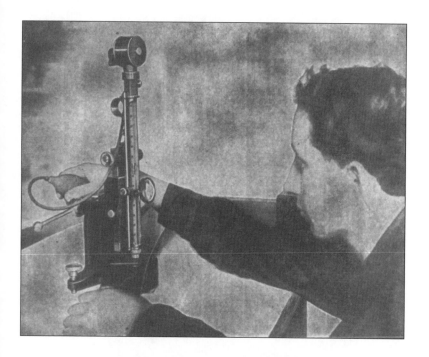

Fig. 188.   Method of Testing Sheets and Flats
Courtesy of Shore Instrument Company, New York City

smooth surface of the metal to be tested, and the height of the rebound of the hammer is taken as the measure of hardness.   The hammer weighs about 40 grains, the height of the rebound from hardened steel is in the neighborhood of 100 on the scale.

While the absolute weight of the entire hammer is little, it is very great relative to the striking area.   The hammer is guided in its fall by a glass tube.   The glass tube is secured to a frame in a vertical position with the lower end upon the test piece.

Fig. 187 shows a complete testing set, and Figs. 188 and 189 the different methods of applying the instrument to different kinds of work.

Fig. 190 gives a general view of the working parts. In the scleroscope action the vital part is the diamond faced drop hammer which must always be raised to its hanger hook at the top where it remains in readiness for the test. In the automatic instrument

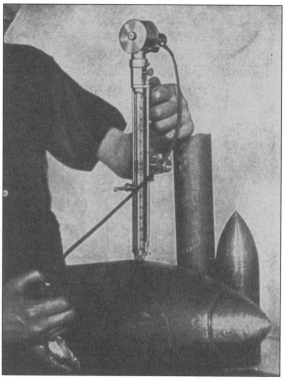

Fig. 189. Testing Hardness of Projectiles
Courtesy of Shore Instrument Company, New York City

now manufactured, the necessary valves, the suction for the hammer and its release all are operated alternately by one bulb acting on the cam *B*, Fig. 190, through the medium of the piston *C*, the adjustable oscillator *D* and the end ratchets *E*. When the hammer is down it will be found impossible to suck it up by the vacuum formed on releasing the hold on the bulb because the valve is then wide open and is held so by the cam *B*.

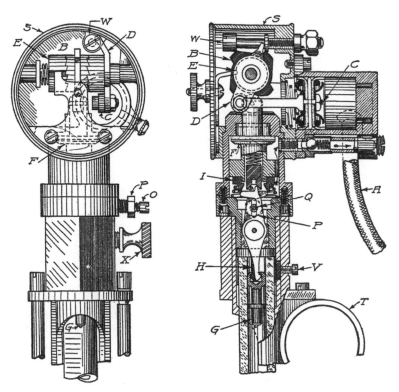

Fig. 190. Detailed Drawing Showing Parts of Shore Scleroscope

TEMPERING

Essentials of Process. To temper steel is to return it to a state of molecular equilibrium at atmospheric temperature by relieving any strains in the metal which have been caused by sudden quenching, and also to correct any exaggeration of certain properties which have been caused by the hardening process. In other words, the object of tempering is to reduce the brittleness in hardened steel, and to remove the internal strains caused by the sudden cooling in the quenching bath. The tempering process consists in heating the piece of work by one of various means to a certain temperature, and in permitting it to cool gradually.

Temperature Conditions. The temperature to which a piece should be raised for tempering depends on several conditions: the use to which it is to be put; the condition in which it has been left by quenching; and the composition of the steel. The degree of heat to which the tool to be tempered is heated determines the degree of toughness it has attained—the higher the tempering heat, the less brittle, and also the less hard, the tool is. The maximum temperature desired need be maintained only long enough to be sure the piece is heated evenly. Steels which are reheated slightly after hardening give a freedom to the molecular change that lessens the molecular rigidity set up by the hardening process.

Reduction of Brittleness. Tools are always left as hard as it is possible to leave them and still have them tough enough for the work for which they are intended. In reducing the brittleness of the steel, some of the hardness is of necessity taken out, and tempering is therefore sometimes spoken of as a reduction of the hardness, but it is in reality merely a reduction of the brittleness. After a tool or piece of steel has been hardened, some of the brittleness is taken out by a slight reheating to a low temperature. These temperatures vary from 200° Fahrenheit, to about 650° Fahrenheit, and are determined in various ways. The simplest and perhaps the most commonly used method is to polish the steel after it has been hardened and then to reheat the part to be tempered until the surface shows a certain color.

If any bright piece of iron or steel is heated, when a temperature of about 400° Fahrenheit is reached, the surface turns pale yellow. As the temperature is increased, this yellow grows darker until at about 500° Fahrenheit it is a decided brown. When 600° Fahrenheit is reached, a deep blue color shows on the surface. These colors are produced by a thin scale which is formed on the surface of the steel and are no indication whatever of hardness, merely showing to what heat steel or iron has been raised.

Baths for Tempering. As the object of tempering is simply to reduce the brittleness and to remove the internal strains caused by the sudden cooling in quenching, the composition of a tempering bath is of little importance as compared with that of a quenching bath. Aside from the operator's convenience and the possible bad effects upon his health, the different baths used for this operation must be considered chiefly with regard to initial cost and lasting quality, and also effect on finish.

Various Mediums. The two main points to be considered

when using an oil tempering furnace are: (1) to have the heat uniform throughout; and (2) to leave the pieces to be tempered in the
oil long enough to have attained the heat of the oil throughout
when they are taken out. While oil is the most widely used medium
for tempering tools in quantities, other means and methods are
employed, especially by those who have tools to temper in small
quantities when the expense of installing and running an oil tem-

Fig. 191. Typical Tempering Furnace
*Courtesy of Strong, Carlisle and Hammond
Company, Cleveland, Ohio*

Fig. 192. S. C.
and H. Company
Thermometer

pering furnace would not be warranted. First there is the old-style
tool hardener's method of only partly cooling the tool when quenching, then quickly withdrawing it, polishing off the working surface,
and letting the heat which remains in the tool produce the required
temper as judged by the color. Heated sand is also used to
produce the temper, likewise using the color scheme as a medium
for judging the degree of hardness. Another common method is

to heat the steel in a bath of red hot lead. The lead is heated in a pot or crucible, to the hardening heat of the steel. The top of the lead is covered with powdered charcoal or coal to prevent the formation of the slag or dross on top. When steel is heated in lead it must be perfectly clean, dry, and free from rust.

Fig. 193. Double Door Furnace for Heating and Annealing Work
Courtesy of Gilbert and Barker Manufacturing Company, Springfield, Massachusetts

Tempering High=Speed Steel. Tools of large size and for hard usage, such as lathe and planer tools, do not require to be tempered, and should be cooled in thin oil such as lard or kerosene oil. In using kerosene oil care should be used not to let a red-hot part be above the surface of the oil, as it will flash; such a piece should be kept in the bath until cooled to the temperature of the oil. Tools like milling cutters, drills, reamers, taps, are generally tempered at from 400° to 500° Fahrenheit, depending on the size, as small tools of the same kind require letting down a little more on hardness.

Furnaces for Tempering. In tempering furnaces, as in all other kinds of furnaces, the really important consideration is to

Fig. 194. Large Size Furnace for Heating, Annealing, and Carbonizing
Courtesy of Strong, Carlisle and Hammond Company, Cleveland, Ohio

insure that the furnace is so built as to heat the bath uniformly. The furnaces for tempering are practically the same as the ones used in hardening; those are the best which permit of maintaining a constant temperature and have appliances for measuring the heat so that the correct temperature can be attained.

Fig. 191 shows an ordinary type of tempering furnace. The general principles of combustion are the same as for the average oil burning furnace, and the tools to be tempered are laid in the receptacle which is immersed in the oil. Fig. 192 shows a thermometer for indicating the temperature of the oil bath. The thermometer is very much like the ordinary mercury thermometer except that it registers as high as 500° to 700° Fahrenheit.

Special Operation. In Figs. 193 and 194 are shown furnaces for heating, annealing, and carbonizing. The burners enter the

Fig. 195. Bottom Brick of Semi-Muffled Furnace
Courtesy of Strong, Carlisle and Hammond Company

Fig. 196. Furnace Bridge
Courtesy of Strong, Carlisle and Hammond Company

combustion chamber underneath the heating oven; the flame strikes a baffle and the tile floor of the oven, and absolute combustion takes place. Heat free from oxidizing properties is produced and is diverted to the heating oven above with a reverberating motion, which produces a uniform circulation; all materials are thoroughly and uniformly heated. The surplus heat is vented through ports on top of the furnace which can be utilized for pre-heating or for

Fig. 197. Brick for Muffled Furnace
Courtesy of Strong, Carlisle and Hammond Company

tempering. Blowers are usually mounted upon brackets in the rear, or they may be placed in any other convenient location. The air receiver is underneath, and compressed air may be used when reduced to the proper pressure.

Advantages of Oil and Gas Types. Oil- and gas-fired furnaces are a great improvement over coke and coal furnaces, as with the latter it is almost impossible to regulate heat to a desired and given point, to say nothing of the inconvenience of shoveling coal and of cleaning out ashes, while dust and dirt that accumulate from these operations are, to say the least, very disagreeable. Then again, steel heated in such furnaces is more liable to scale or oxidize and to absorb some of the sulphur and

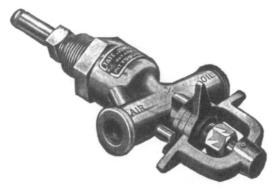

Fig. 198.   Oil Burner without Air Blast Connection
Courtesy of Tate, Jones and Company, Pittsburgh, Pennsylvania

other impurities that arise from the combustion. It is a well-known fact that steel absorbs those injurious elements readily at a heat high enough for hardening and working. In a good gas or oil furnace the heat can be very closely regulated, so that the variation is not more than 10 or 15 degrees, which is close enough for most ordinary work.

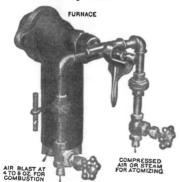

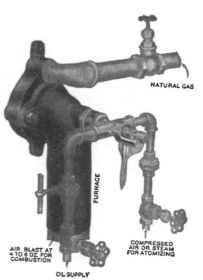

Fig. 199.   Oil Burner with Air Blast and Compressed Air and Steam Connection for Atomizing
Courtesy of Tate, Jones and Company, Pittsburgh, Pennsylvania

Fig. 200.   Burner Similar to Fig. 199, with Natural Gas Connection
Courtesy of Tate, Jones and Company, Pittsburgh, Pennsylvania

Oil-Burning Furnace.   Although the installation is more costly
than that of a gas furnace, oil furnaces are used a good deal for
economy by large concerns.   A storage tank under ground is generally used together with a pumping system to maintain a pressure

Figs. 201 and 202.   Front and Back View of Gas Burner
Courtesy of Tate, Jones and Company, Pittsburgh

Fig. 203.   S., C. and H.
Cast-Iron Pot

sufficient for forcing the oil to the furnace.   The oil flows through
a simple regulating valve and is immediately atomized with either
steam or air at a pressure of from 35 to 100 pounds per square inch.
At this point it enters the forcing hood in the form of fine mist
where a volume of air at a pressure of about 6 to 15 ounces per square

Fig. 204.   Cast-Iron Pot
Used for Lead Pot

Fig. 205.   Wire Basket for Immersing Work
in Oil Bath

inch carries it along the combustion chamber in which it ignites
and burns with an intense heat.

A good design of burner should have eliminated the trouble-
some features of sputtering and dripping oil, which cause an irregular
flame.   The flame should be clear, white, and free from smoke, soot,
and dirt.

Details of Muffle Furnace.   In Fig. 195 is shown the bottom
brick of a semi-muffle furnace.   Fig. 196 shows another brick which
is called the furnace bridge.   Fig. 197 shows the furnace brick for

this furnace.   The heating chamber is enclosed entirely.   Parts to be heated do not come in contact with the furnace flame.

Burners.   In Fig. 198 is shown a burner without blast connections for use where air blast is not available.   This is used by attaching the burner in such a way that air for combustion is drawn into the furnace by the injector effect of the atomized oil.   In Fig. 199 is shown an oil burner with blast connections. The supply of oil and the compressed air for atomizing are regulated by one lever. Fig. 200 shows the same burner with natural gas attachment.   This burner is just as efficient a gas burner as it is an oil burner.   Figs. 201 and 202 show different views of gas burners.   An air blast is introduced in the back of the burner.

Fig. 206.   Special Pot for Annealing or Casehardening
Courtesy of Strong, Carlisle and Hammond Company, Cleveland, Ohio

Containers.   Fig. 203 shows a cast-iron pot which can be used for a number of things.   Fig. 204 shows a cast-iron pot used for a lead pot.   Fig. 205 shows a wire basket for immersing work to be tempered in the oil bath, or it may be used as a basket for holding small tools after hardening.   Fig. 206 shows a pot for either annealing or casehardening.

INDEX

PAGE

A

Angle welding.. 27
Annealing.. 98
    copper and brass.. 100
    general process... 98
    high-speed steel.. 99
Anvils.. 10

B

Bend forging (simple)... 29
    bend types.. 35
    calculation of stock for bent shapes............................... 33
    fundamental forging operations.................................... 29
Bend types in forging... 35
    bend with square-forged corner.................................... 37
    bolts.. 42
    chain hooks... 40
    eye bolts.. 39
    forming shoulders... 38
    hoisting hooks.. 41
    ladles.. 47
    ring and eye bending.. 35
    twisted gate hook... 37
Blacksmith's tools.. 78
Bolt headers... 19
Brazing.. 80
Brinell tester... 120
Bulldozer.. 19
Butt welding... 26

C

Carbonizing.. 105
    boxes for packing... 109
    casehardening problem.. 105
    general packing... 109
    hardening with one heat... 109
    materials.. 106
    principles of process.. 106
    re-using carbonizing material...................................... 109
    temperature... 109
    use of crucible.. 107
Casehardening... 113
    problem of... 105
Cast iron, bending.. 81
Cold chisels... 67

INDEX

	PAGE
Common tools	9
anvils	10
fullers	14
hammers	9
other tools	14
set hammers and flatters	13
sledges	10
swage blocks	14
swages	13
tongs	12
Cranes	19
Crank shafts	54
Cyanide hardening	112
casehardening	113
potassium-cyanide bath	112

D

Die forging	83
Drop forging	90
drop hammers	92
process	92
specimens	92
Drop hammers	15, 92
Duplicate work	82

F

Fluxes	21
Forges	2
Forging	1–131
common tools	9
heat treatment	93
heating apparatus	2
machine tools	15
materials and equipment	1
classification	2
mechanical details	1
operations	20
Forging heat	67
Forging materials	1
Forging operations	20
angle welding	27
butt welding	26
drop forging	90
heavy forging	85
lap welding	22
medium forged work	49
miscellaneous processes	78
bending cast iron	81
brazing	80

INDEX

PAGE

Forging operations (continued)
    miscellaneous processes
        die forging... 83
        duplicate work... 82
        pipe bending.. 81
        shrinking.. 78
    scarfing... 22
    simple bending forging.. 29
    smith welding.. 20
    split welding heavy stock... 27
    T-welding.. 28
    tool-steel work... 67
    welding tool steel.. 28
Forging operations (fundamental)... 29
    drawing out.. 29
    punching... 32
    shaping.. 29
    truing up work... 31
    upsetting.. 31
Fullers... 14
Furnaces... 7

H

Hammer chisels.. 86
Hammer dies.. 85
Hammers..9, 76
    ball-peen... 77
    riveting.. 76
Hardening... 100
    bath... 102
    carbonizing.. 105
    cracks and fissures... 104
    cyanide hardening.. 112
    essential features.. 100
    heat treatment after carbonizing.. 110
        shell and core distinction.................................... 110
        specimens.. 112
    influencing factors... 101
    measuring and testing instruments.. 116
    preparatory heating.. 101
    purpose.. 100
    quenching tanks... 103
    results... 101
    tool work.. 113
    warping.. 105
Heat treatment.. 93
    annealing.. 98
    factors in.. 94
    hardening.. 100

INDEX

PAGE

Heat treatment (continued)
    heating for forging... 96
    processes of treating.. 96
    steel development, relation to................................. 93
    tempering... 123
Heating apparatus... 2
    forges.. 2
    furnaces.. 7
Heavy forging... 85
    examples of work.. 89
    hammer chisels.. 86
    hammer dies... 85
    squaring up work.. 88
    steam hammer.. 85
    tongs... 86
    tools... 87

I

Instruments, measuring and testing................................ 116
    Brinell tester.. 120
    hardness testing.. 119
    pyrometers.. 116
    Shore scleroscope... 121

K

Knuckles.. 59

L

Ladle shank... 63
Lap welding... 22
    allowance for welding... 24
    band ring... 25
    chain links... 25
    flat or washer ring... 26
    ring round stock.. 24
    round lap weld.. 24
Lathe tools... 69
Lever with boss... 58

M

Machine tools... 15
    bolt headers.. 19
    bulldozer... 19
    cranes.. 19
    drop hammers.. 15
    manufacturing requirement..................................... 15
    power hammers... 16
    presses... 18

INDEX

                                                              PAGE
Medium forged work... 49
    calculation of stock................................... 49
        finish... 52
        stock changed in shape.......................... 49
        weight of forging............................... 51
    standard large types................................... 54
        crank shafts..................................... 54
        knuckles... 59
        ladle shank...................................... 63
        lever with boss.................................. 58
        molder's trowel.................................. 65
        weldless rings................................... 57
        wrenches... 60
Molder's trowel.. 65

P

Pipe bending... 81
Potassium-cyanide bath... 112
Power hammers.. 16
Presses.. 18
Pyrometers... 116

S

Scale.. 21
Scarfing... 22
Set hammers and flatters....................................... 13
Shore scleroscope.. 121
Shrinking.. 78
Sledges.. 10
Smith welding.. 20
      fluxes... 21
      nature of process................................ 20
      scale.. 21
      welding heat..................................... 20
Split welding heavy stock...................................... 27
Springs.. 75
Steam hammer... 85
Steel development, relation to................................. 93
Stock for bent shapes, calculation of.......................... 33
    mathematical calculation............................... 33
    measurement by dividers................................ 35
    measurement by string or wire.......................... 35
    measuring wheel.. 34
Swage blocks... 14
Swages... 13

T

Tables
    casehardening.. 109
    color scale of iron heats.............................. 79

INDEX

PAGE

Tables (continued)
    sizes of hoisting hooks.. 41
    weight of flat rolled iron... 51
Tempering.. 123
    baths for... 124
    essentials of process... 123
    furnaces for.. 127
    high-speed steel.. 126
    reduction of brittleness.. 124
Tongs..12, 86
Tool work.. 113
    hardening heat.. 114
    hardening high-speed steel.. 115
    laws for hardening.. 113
Tool-steel work.. 67
    proper forging heat... 67
    standard forms.. 67
        blacksmith's tools.. 78
        cold chisels... 67
        hammers.. 76
        lathe tools.. 69
        springs.. 75
Tools.. 87
T-welding.. 28

W

Welding heat... 20
Welding tool steel... 28
Weldless rings... 57
Wrenches... 60